Ikenaga 2 Jos Leys

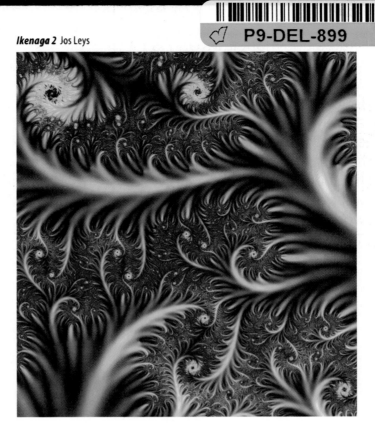

"A relatively simple formula can generate immensely complex images." – **Jos Leys**

GRADE **3**

Perimeter, Angles, and Area

2-D Geometry and Measurement   UNIT **4**

Investigations
IN NUMBER, DATA, AND SPACE®

PEARSON
Scott
Foresman
scottforesman.com

Editorial offices: Glenview, Illinois • Parsippany, New Jersey • New York, New York
Sales offices: Boston, Massachusetts • Duluth, Georgia
Glenview, Illinois • Coppell, Texas • Sacramento, California • Mesa, Arizona

T E R C

The Investigations curriculum was developed by TERC, Cambridge, MA.

This material is based on work supported by the National Science Foundation ("NSF") under Grant No. ESI-0095450. Any opinions, findings, and conclusions or recommendations expressed in this material are those of the author(s) and do not necessarily reflect the views of the National Science Foundation.

ISBN: 0-328-23747-7

ISBN: 978-0-328-23747-0

7 8 9 10-V003-15 14 13 12 11 10 09 08
CC:N2

T E R C

Co-Principal Investigators

Susan Jo Russell

Karen Economopoulos

Authors

Lucy Wittenberg
Director Grades 3–5

Karen Economopoulos
Director Grades K–2

Virginia Bastable
(SummerMath for Teachers,
Mt. Holyoke College)

Katie Hickey Bloomfield

Keith Cochran

Darrell Earnest

Arusha Hollister

Nancy Horowitz

Erin Leidl

Megan Murray

Young Oh

Beth W. Perry

Susan Jo Russell

Deborah Schifter
(Education
Development Center)

Kathy Sillman

Administrative Staff

Amy Taber
Project Manager

Beth Bergeron

Lorraine Brooks

Emi Fujiwara

Contributing Authors

Denise Baumann

Jennifer DiBrienza

Hollee Freeman

Paula Hooper

Jan Mokros

Stephen Monk
(University of Washington)

Mary Beth O'Connor

Judy Storeygard

Cornelia Tierney

Elizabeth Van Cleef

Carol Wright

Technology

Jim Hammerman

Classroom Field Work

Amy Appell

Rachel E. Davis

Traci Higgins

Julia Thompson

Collaborating Teachers

This group of dedicated teachers carried out extensive field testing in their classrooms, met regularly to discuss issues of teaching and learning mathematics, provided feedback to staff, welcomed staff into their classrooms to document students' work, and contributed both suggestions and written material that has been incorporated into the curriculum.

Bethany Altchek

Linda Amaral

Kimberly Beauregard

Barbara Bernard

Nancy Buell

Rose Christiansen

Chris Colbath-Hess

Lisette Colon

Kim Cook

Frances Cooper

Kathleen Drew

Rebeka Eston Salemi

Thomas Fisher

Michael Flynn

Holly Ghazey

Susan Gillis

Danielle Harrington

Elaine Herzog

Francine Hiller

Kirsten Lee Howard

Liliana Klass

Leslie Kramer

Melissa Lee Andrichak

Kelley Lee Sadowski

Jennifer Levitan

Mary Lou LoVecchio

Kristen McEnaney

Maura McGrail

Kathe Millett

Florence Molyneaux

Amy Monkiewicz

Elizabeth Monopoli

Carol Murray

Robyn Musser

Christine Norrman

Deborah O'Brien

Timothy O'Connor

Anne Marie O'Reilly

Mark Paige

Margaret Riddle

Karen Schweitzer

Elisabeth Seyferth

Susan Smith

Debra Sorvillo

Shoshanah Starr

Janice Szymaszek

Karen Tobin

JoAnn Trauschke

Ana Vaisenstein

Yvonne Watson

Michelle Woods

Mary Wright

Note: Unless otherwise noted, all contributors listed above were staff of the Education Research Collaborative at TERC during their work on the curriculum. Other affiliations during the time of development are listed.

Advisors

Deborah Lowenberg Ball,
University of Michigan

Hyman Bass, Professor of Mathematics and Mathematics Education
University of Michigan

Mary Canner, Principal, Natick Public Schools

Thomas Carpenter, Professor of Curriculum and Instruction,
University of Wisconsin-Madison

Janis Freckmann, Elementary Mathematics Coordinator,
Milwaukee Public Schools

Lynne Godfrey, Mathematics Coach,
Cambridge Public Schools

Ginger Hanlon, Instructional Specialist in Mathematics,
New York City Public Schools

DeAnn Huinker, Director, Center for Mathematics and
Science Education Research, University of Wisconsin-Milwaukee

James Kaput, Professor of Mathematics, University of
Massachusetts-Dartmouth

Kate Kline, Associate Professor, Department of Mathematics
and Statistics, Western Michigan University

Jim Lewis, Professor of Mathematics,
University of Nebraska-Lincoln

William McCallum, Professor of Mathematics,
University of Arizona

Harriet Pollatsek, Professor of Mathematics,
Mount Holyoke College

Debra Shein-Gerson, Elementary Mathematics Specialist,
Weston Public Schools

Gary Shevell, Assistant Principal,
New York City Public Schools

Liz Sweeney, Elementary Math Department,
Boston Public Schools

Lucy West, Consultant, Metamorphosis:
Teaching Learning Communities, Inc.

This revision of the curriculum was built on the work of the many authors who contributed to the first edition (published between 1994 and 1998). We acknowledge the critical contributions of these authors in developing the content and pedagogy of *Investigations*:

Authors

Joan Akers

Michael T. Battista

Douglas H. Clements

Karen Economopoulos

Marlene Kliman

Jan Mokros

Megan Murray

Ricardo Nemirovsky

Andee Rubin

Susan Jo Russell

Cornelia Tierney

Contributing Authors

Mary Berle-Carman

Rebecca B. Corwin

Rebeka Eston

Claryce Evans

Anne Goodrow

Cliff Konold

Chris Mainhart

Sue McMillen

Jerrie Moffet

Tracy Noble

Kim O'Neil

Mark Ogonowski

Julie Sarama

Amy Shulman Weinberg

Margie Singer

Virginia Woolley

Tracey Wright

Contents

UNIT 4

Perimeter, Angles, and Area

Overview of Program Components

FOR TEACHERS

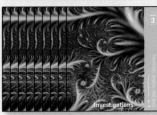

The **Curriculum Units** are the teaching guides. (See far right.)

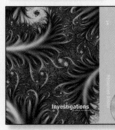

Implementing Investigations in Grade 3 offers suggestions for implementing the curriculum. It also contains a comprehensive index.

The **Resources Binder** contains all the Resource Masters and Transparencies that support instruction. (Also available on CD) The binder also includes a student software CD.

FOR STUDENTS

The **Student Activity Book** contains the consumable student pages (Recording Sheets, Homework, Practice, and so on).

The **Student Math Handbook** contains Math Words and Ideas pages and Games directions.

The *Investigations* Curriculum

Investigations in Number, Data, and Space® is a K–5 mathematics curriculum designed to engage students in making sense of mathematical ideas. Six major goals guided the development of the *Investigations in Number, Data, and Space®* curriculum. The curriculum is designed to:

• Support students to make sense of mathematics and learn that they can be mathematical thinkers

• Focus on computational fluency with whole numbers as a major goal of the elementary grades

• Provide substantive work in important areas of mathematics—rational numbers, geometry, measurement, data, and early algebra—and connections among them

• Emphasize reasoning about mathematical ideas

• Communicate mathematics content and pedagogy to teachers

• Engage the range of learners in understanding mathematics

Underlying these goals are three guiding principles that are touchstones for the *Investigations* team as we approach both students and teachers as agents of their own learning:

1. *Students have mathematical ideas.* Students come to school with ideas about numbers, shapes, measurements, patterns, and data. If given the opportunity to learn in an environment that stresses making sense of mathematics, students build on the ideas they already have and learn about new mathematics they have never encountered. Students learn that they are capable of having mathematical ideas, applying what they know to new situations, and thinking and reasoning about unfamiliar problems.

2. *Teachers are engaged in ongoing learning* about mathematics content, pedagogy, and student learning. The curriculum provides material for professional development, to be used by teachers individually or in groups, that supports teachers' continued learning as they use the curriculum over several years. The *Investigations* curriculum materials are designed as much to be a dialogue with teachers as to be a core of content for students.

3. *Teachers collaborate with the students and curriculum materials* to create the curriculum as enacted in the classroom. The only way for a good curriculum to be used well is for teachers to be active participants in implementing it. Teachers use the curriculum to maintain a clear, focused, and coherent agenda for mathematics teaching. At the same time, they observe and listen carefully to students, try to understand how they are thinking, and make teaching decisions based on these observations.

Investigations is based on experience from research and practice, including field testing that involved documentation of thousands of hours in classrooms, observations of students, input from teachers, and analysis of student work. As a result, the curriculum addresses the learning needs of real students in a wide range of classrooms and communities. The investigations are carefully designed to invite all students into mathematics—girls and boys; members of diverse cultural, ethnic, and language groups; and students with a wide variety of strengths, needs, and interests.

Based on this extensive classroom testing, the curriculum takes seriously the time students need to develop a strong conceptual foundation and skills based on that foundation. Each curriculum unit focuses on an area of content in depth, providing time for students to develop and practice ideas across a variety of activities and contexts that build on each other. Daily guidelines for time spent on class sessions, Classroom Routines (K–3), and Ten-Minute Math (3–5) reflect the commitment to devoting adequate time to mathematics in each school day.

About This Curriculum Unit

This **Curriculum Unit** is one of nine teaching guides in Grade 3. The fourth unit in Grade 3 is *Perimeter, Angles, and Area.*

- The **Introduction and Overview** section organizes and presents the instructional materials, provides background information, and highlights important features specific to this unit.

- Each Curriculum Unit contains several **Investigations.** Each Investigation focuses on a set of related mathematical ideas.

- Investigations are divided into one-hour **Sessions,** or lessons.

- Sessions have a combination of these parts: **Activity, Discussion, Math Workshop, Assessment Activity,** and **Session Follow-Up.**

- Each session also has one or more **Classroom Routines** and **Ten-Minute Math** activities that are done outside of math time.

- At the back of the book is a collection of **Teacher Notes** and **Dialogue Boxes** that provide professional development related to the unit.

- Also included at the back of the book are the **Student Math Handbook** pages for this unit.

- The **Index** provides a way to look up important words or terms.

Overview

OF THIS UNIT

Investigation	Session	Day	
INVESTIGATION 1 ### Linear Measurement Students develop their ability to use measurement tools to accurately measure objects. They learn that perimeter is the distance around the outside edges of a 2-dimensional figure and that it is measured.	**1.1** Using U.S. and Metric Units to Measure Length	1	
	1.2 Introducing Perimeter	2	
	1.3 Assessment: Measuring Perimeter	3	
	1.4 Perimeter Problems	4	
	1.5 Ordering Shapes by Perimeter	5	
INVESTIGATION 2 ### Understanding and Finding Area Students identify the amount of space a given object covers as its area, and develop an understanding that area is measured in square units. They use this knowledge to measure an irregular area—their footprint.	**2.1** Tetrominoes	6	
	2.2 Which Tetrominoes Fit?	7	
	2.3 Squares and Triangles	8	
	2.4 Area Activities	9	
	2.5 Area Activities, *continued*	10	
	2.6 Assessment: Make a Shape	11	
INVESTIGATION 3 ### Triangles, Quadrilaterals, and Angles Students identify various attributes of shapes and learn that the number of sides identifies a shape as a triangle or a quadrilateral. They identify right angles as having a measure of 90 degrees and learn that angle size is independent of figure size.	**3.1** Triangles	12	
	3.2 Is It a Triangle?	13	
	3.3 Squares, Rectangles, and Other Quadrilaterals	14	
	3.4 Angles of Different Sizes	15	
	3.5 Working with Shapes and Angles	16	
	3.6 End-of-Unit Assessment	17	

Each *Investigations* session has some combination of these five parts: **Activity, Discussion, Math Workshop, Assessment Activity,** and **Session Follow-Up.** These session parts are indicated in the chart below. Each session also has one or more **Classroom Routines** and **Ten-Minute Math** activities that are done outside of math time.

Activity	Discussion	Math Workshop	Assessment Activity	Session Follow-Up	Practicing Place Value	Quick Images
●●	●			●	●	
●●	●			●	●	
●	●	●	●	●	●	
	●	●		●	●	
●	●	●		●	●	
●●	●			●		●
●	●●			●		●
●●●	●			●		●
●	●	●		●	●	
●	●	●		●	●	
	●	●	●	●		●
●●	●			●		●
●●	●			●	●	
●	●	●		●		●
●	●			●		●
	●	●		●	●	
			●	●	●	

(Ten-Minute Math columns: *Practicing Place Value*, *Quick Images*)

Mathematics

IN THIS UNIT

Perimeter, Angles, and Area is the first Grade 3 unit in the Geometry and Measurement strand of *Investigations.* These units develop ideas about the attributes of 2-dimensional (2-D) and 3-dimensional (3-D) shapes, and help students understand how these attributes determine their classification. They also develop ideas about linear measurement (which includes perimeter), square measurement (area), the measurement of angles, and volume.

The work in this unit assumes that students have developed an understanding of the need for standard units of measure and a familiarity with the use of rulers, yardsticks, and metersticks to measure length. Students entering Grade 3 should be familiar with 2-dimensional shapes such as triangles, squares, and rectangles. They should be able to identify some of the attributes of these shapes (e.g., that squares have right angles and four equal sides). The area work in this unit is based on students' prior experiences in Grades K–2 fitting together shapes to make other shapes (e.g., using pattern blocks to fill in outlines of given shapes) and creating rectangular arrays with a given number of square tiles.

This unit focuses on 5 Mathematical Emphases:

1 Linear Measurement **Measuring with standard units**

Math Focus Points

◆ Reviewing the length of units of measure (inch, foot, yard, centimeter, and meter)

◆ Establishing measurement benchmarks

◆ Using U.S. standard and metric units to accurately measure length

◆ Recognizing and explaining possible sources of measurement error

In the United States, the conventional units of length are inches, feet, yards, and miles. However, most countries in the world that use the metric system use centimeters, meters, and kilometers as units of length. In this unit, students become accustomed to both systems: using rulers and yardsticks to measure in inches, feet, and yards, and using centimeter rulers and metersticks to measure in centimeters and meters.

Measuring length accurately involves learning about measurement ideas and techniques. Measurement ideas include identifying a unit of measure, such as an inch or a centimeter, and then determining how many of those units fit the length to be measured. Another important measurement idea is that when the same length is measured with different units, a different count of units is found. Students measure the same length in both inches and centimeters and consider why the results differ. They begin to understand why it is true that the smaller the unit of measure, the greater the count for the same length.

In this unit, students continue to develop their ability to use measurement tools as they work on accurate measurement techniques, such as accurate placement of a measurement tool next to the object to be measured, placement of the tool without gaps or overlaps, keeping track of partial units, and calculating a total distance.

2 Linear Measurement **Understanding and finding perimeter**

Math Focus Points

◆ Understanding perimeter as the measure around the outside edges of a 2-dimensional figure

◆ Finding perimeter using standard units

◆ Creating different shapes with the same perimeter

◆ Finding the perimeter of an irregular shape

In Investigation 1, students learn that the distance around the outside edges of a 2-dimensional figure is called the perimeter. One way to think about perimeter is to imagine a piece of string wrapped around a 2-dimensional shape. If the object is a polygon, such as a rectangle or a triangle with side lengths that are known, the perimeter can be found by adding the side lengths.

Students develop and apply their understanding of perimeter as they measure the perimeter of some 2-D surfaces of objects in the classroom. In addition, they consider how and why different shapes can have the same perimeter.

3 Area Measurement Understanding and finding area

Math Focus Points

◈ Understanding that area is measured in square units

◈ Understanding that when measuring area, the space being measured must be completely covered with no gaps or overlaps

◈ Using squares and triangles to make shapes with an area of four square units

◈ Examining the relationship between the area of squares and triangles

◈ Understanding that shapes with the same area can look different

◈ Finding the area of partially covered rectangles

◈ Finding the area of an irregular shape

◈ Designing a shape for a given area

◈ Finding area by counting or calculating whole and partial square units

Area, unlike perimeter, is not a linear measure. Because area involves covering space, the unit of area must also cover space. In Investigation 2, students identify the amount of space a given object covers as its *area,* and learn that area is measured in square units. For instance, the area of the rectangle below is six square units.

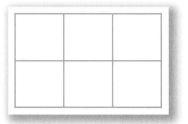

When figures cannot be easily decomposed into squares, the area is still reported in terms of square units. Students use squares and triangles to make shapes with a given area and examine the areas of squares and triangles. They push this understanding further as they find the area of an irregular shape—their footprint. In this activity, students find that it is necessary to choose a square unit of some size, superimpose a grid of the square units, and then find the area by counting squares and partial squares.

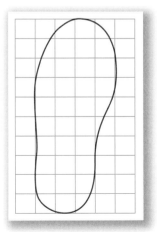

4 Features of Shape Describing and classifying 2-dimensional figures

Math Focus Points

◆ Determining the geometric moves needed (slides, flips, turns) to prove or disprove congruence between two shapes

◆ Identifying the attributes of triangles: three sides, three vertices, and three angles

◆ Identifying the attributes of quadrilaterals: four sides, four vertices, and four angles

◆ Comparing the properties of squares and rectangles

One way to describe shapes is by noting whether or not they are *congruent* to other shapes. At the beginning of Investigation 2, students create a variety of arrangements of four squares, or *tetrominoes.* They then work to determine whether or not any of the arrangements they created are *congruent,* or exactly the same size and shape. In this activity, they encounter the idea of geometric motions—*slides* (translations), *flips* (reflections), and *turns* (rotations). These motions account for all of the ways we can move 2-dimensional shapes. Students find that if shapes are congruent, there is a sequence of slides, flips, and turns that will move one exactly onto the other.

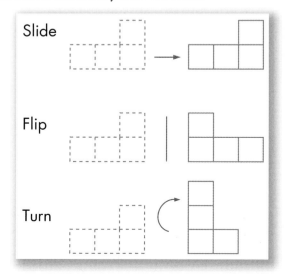

Students also work on the classification of shapes. Understanding that a shape is classified as a triangle or a quadrilateral on the basis of the number of sides and not what the shape looks like is an important idea in this unit. Many students associate the word "triangle" with a visual pattern, something like Figure A below. While they recognize that Figures B and C also have three sides, the other attributes such as the orientation of the shape or the size of the angles may lead them to question whether the shape can still be named "triangle." In Investigation 3 of this unit, students identify various attributes of shapes and determine that the number of sides is the only mathematically significant attribute when identifying a shape as a triangle or a quadrilateral.

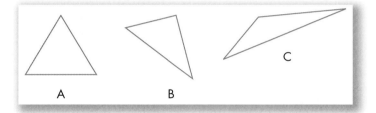

Students also begin to work with the idea that one shape may have more than one name as they compare the properties of squares and rectangles.

5 Features of Shape Describing and measuring angles

Math Focus Points

◆ Recognizing right angles

◆ Identifying a right angle as having a measure of 90 degrees

◆ Understanding angle size as the degree of turn

◆ Comparing the sizes of angles

One attribute of polygons examined in this unit is angle. In the triangles above, Figure A has angles that are equal to one another. In Figure B, one of the angles appears to be a right angle (90°), and in Figure C, one of the angles is much greater than 90°.

The work in this unit focuses on helping students form ideas about angles. Although students became familiar with right angles as the kind of angle in a rectangle or square in Grade 2, it is in this unit that they identify these angles as measuring 90°. Students also use right angles as a benchmark as they consider the sizes of angles relative to 90°. Two other aspects of angles are considered—that an angle of a polygon is formed by two of the sides and that angle size is independent of figure size. For instance, consider these two figures:

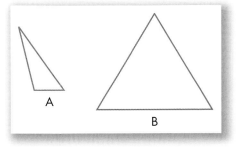

One of the angles in Figure A is larger than any of the angles in Figure B, even though Figure B is larger in size than Figure A.

Classroom Routines focus on

◆ Learning about temperature: reading a thermometer, learning to associate different temperatures with words like *colder* and *warmer*, and establishing landmark temperatures

◆ Recording information in a table and on a graph

◆ Reading information from the shape of a graph: hot, cold, increasing, decreasing

Ten-Minute Math activities focus on

◆ Recognizing and interpreting the value of each digit in 3-digit numbers

◆ Finding different combinations of numbers, such as 100s, 10s, and 1s, that are equivalent, (i.e., 1 hundred, 3 tens, and 7 ones = 1 hundred, 2 tens, and 17 ones = 13 tens and 7 ones = 12 tens and 17 ones, and so on)

◆ Reading and writing numbers up to 1,000

◆ Adding multiples of 10 to, and subtracting multiples of 10 from 3-digit numbers

◆ Organizing and analyzing visual images

◆ Developing language and concepts needed to communicate about spatial relationships

◆ Decomposing images of 2-D shapes and then recombining them to make a given design

LOOKING FORWARD Students draw on the measurement work in this unit as they continue to measure longer distances and to measure length with a variety of units in Grades 4 and 5.

Classifying shapes by deciding what attributes are significant is an important part of developing a sense of the relationships among polygons (for instance, that all squares are rectangles but not all rectangles are squares) and determining how to define terms such as square, rectangle, and rhombus. The work in this unit on identifying attributes of shape is the basis for the Grades 4 and 5 work on classifying and categorizing polygons.

In Grades 4 and 5, students will also continue to work with the idea that a given 2-dimensional object has more than one measurement. For a given shape, its perimeter, its area, the size of its angles, or the lengths of its sides can all be measured. The early work in this unit with perimeter and area will be the basis for future work as students determine methods to measure the perimeter and area of more complicated polygons.

Technology Note

Introducing the Software The *LogoPaths* Software is introduced to students in this unit. If you are planning to use the software, you will need to familiarize yourself with it. For information about the *LogoPaths* software, refer to the *Software Support Reference Guide* found on the CD. To prepare to integrate this work into your classroom and to manage the computer environment, see **Teacher Note:** Introducing and Managing the *LogoPaths* Software, page 139, and **Teacher Note:** About the Mathematics in the *LogoPaths* Software, page 142, for further support and information.

Assessment

IN THIS UNIT

ONGOING ASSESSMENT: Observing Students at Work

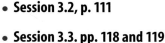

The following sessions provide **Ongoing Assessment: Observing Students at Work** opportunities:

- **Session 1.1, p. 26**
- **Session 1.2, pp. 31 and 35**
- **Session 1.3, pp. 40 and 41**
- **Session 1.4, pp. 48 and 49**
- **Session 2.1, pp. 64 and 67**
- **Session 2.2, p. 72**

- **Session 2.3, p. 77**
- **Session 2.4, pp. 84 and 85**
- **Session 2.5, p. 92**
- **Session 2.6, p. 95**
- **Session 3.1, p. 106–107**

- **Session 3.2, p. 111**
- **Session 3.3. pp. 118 and 119**
- **Session 3.4, p. 127**
- **Session 3.5, p. 130**
- **Session 3.6, p. 135**

WRITING OPPORTUNITIES

The following sessions have **writing** opportunities for students to explain their mathematical thinking:

- **Session 1.1, p. 28**
  Student Activity Book, pp. 3–4
- **Session 1.3, p. 39**
  Student Activity Book, pp. 9–10
- **Session 2.1, p. 67**
  Student Activity Book, p. 20

- **Session 2.4, p. 84**
  Student Activity Book, pp. 29–30
- **Session 2.5, p. 89**
  Student Activity Book, p. 33

- **Session 3.2, p. 111**
  Student Activity Book, p. 41
- **Session 3.3, p. 118**
  Student Activity Book, pp. 45–46

PORTFOLIO OPPORTUNITIES

The following sessions have work appropriate for a **portfolio:**

- **Session 1.3, p. 40**
  M15, Assessment: Measuring Perimeter
- **Session 1.4, p. 47**
  Student Activity Book, pp. 12–13

- **Session 2.5, p. 89**
  Student Activity Book, p. 33
- **Session 2.6, p. 95**
  M20, Assessment: Make a Shape

- **Session 3.4, p. 126**
  Student Activity Book, pp. 49–50
- **Session 3.6, p. 135**
  M22–M24, End-of-Unit Assessment

Assessing the Benchmarks

Observing students as they engage in conversation about their ideas is a primary means to assess their mathematical understanding. Consider all of your students' work, not just the written assessments. See the chart below for suggestions about key activities to observe.

☑ Checklist Available

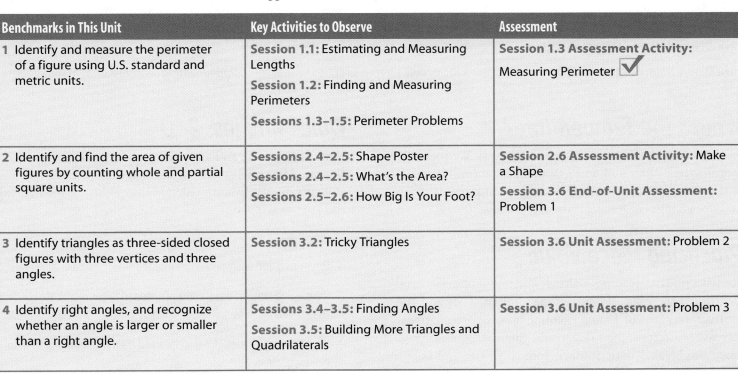

Benchmarks in This Unit	Key Activities to Observe	Assessment
1 Identify and measure the perimeter of a figure using U.S. standard and metric units.	**Session 1.1:** Estimating and Measuring Lengths **Session 1.2:** Finding and Measuring Perimeters **Sessions 1.3–1.5:** Perimeter Problems	**Session 1.3 Assessment Activity:** Measuring Perimeter ☑
2 Identify and find the area of given figures by counting whole and partial square units.	**Sessions 2.4–2.5:** Shape Poster **Sessions 2.4–2.5:** What's the Area? **Sessions 2.5–2.6:** How Big Is Your Foot?	**Session 2.6 Assessment Activity:** Make a Shape **Session 3.6 End-of-Unit Assessment:** Problem 1
3 Identify triangles as three-sided closed figures with three vertices and three angles.	**Session 3.2:** Tricky Triangles	**Session 3.6 Unit Assessment:** Problem 2
4 Identify right angles, and recognize whether an angle is larger or smaller than a right angle.	**Sessions 3.4–3.5:** Finding Angles **Session 3.5:** Building More Triangles and Quadrilaterals	**Session 3.6 Unit Assessment:** Problem 3

Relating the Mathematical Emphases to the Benchmarks

Mathematical Emphases	Benchmarks
Linear Measurement Measuring with standard units	1
Linear Measurement Understanding and finding perimeter	1
Area Measurement Understanding and finding area	2
Features of Shape Describing and classifying 2-dimensional figures	3
Features of Shape Describing and measuring angles	4

Classroom Routines and Ten-Minute Math

The **Classroom Routines** and **Ten-Minute Math** activities, to be done in ten minutes outside of math class, are introduced in a unit and repeated throughout the grade. Specific directions for the day's activity are provided in each session. For the full description and variations of the Classroom Routines and Ten-Minute Math activities, see *Implementing Investigations in Grade 3*.

Activity	Introduced	Full Description of Activity and Its Variations
Classroom Routines: *What's the Temperature?*	Unit 1, Session 1.1	*Implementing Investigations in Grade 3*
Ten-Minute Math: *Practicing Place Value*	Unit 1, Session 1.1	*Implementing Investigations in Grade 3*
Ten-Minute Math: *Quick Images: 2-D*	Unit 4, Session 1.5 (this unit)	*Implementing Investigations in Grade 3*

What's the Temperature?

Students record the outside temperature every Wednesday morning on a chart and on a graph. This data will be used in the unit *Stories, Tables, and Graphs,* when students describe changes in temperature over time.

Practicing Place Value

Students practice reading, writing, and saying numbers and identifying the value of digits in the number. They add and subtract multiples of 10 and examine how these operations increase or decrease the values of the digits in each place. They also break 3-digit numbers into 100s, 10s, and 1s in different ways.

Math Focus Points

- Recognizing and interpreting the value of each digit in 3-digit numbers

- Finding different combinations of a number, using only 100s, 10s, and 1s and recognizing their equivalence (i.e., 1 hundred, 3 tens, and 7 ones = 1 hundred, 2 tens, and 17 ones = 13 tens and 7 ones = 12 tens and 17 ones, etc.)

- Reading and writing numbers up to 1,000

- Adding multiples of 10 to, and subtracting multiples of 10 from 3-digit numbers

Quick Images: 2–D

Students visualize and analyze images of 2-D geometric figures. After briefly viewing an image of a 2-D design, students draw it from the mental image they formed during the brief viewing.

Math Focus Points

- Organizing and analyzing visual images

- Developing language and concepts needed to communicate about spatial relationships

- Decomposing images of 2-D shapes and then recombining them to make a given design

Practice and Review

IN THIS UNIT

Practice and review play a critical role in the *Investigations* program. The following components and features are available to provide regular reinforcement of key mathematical concepts and procedures.

Books	Features	In This Unit . . .
Curriculum Unit	**The Classroom Routines** and **Ten-Minute Math** activities, to be done in ten minutes outside of math class, are introduced in a unit and repeated throughout the grade. Specific directions for the day's activity are provided in each session. For the full description and variations of the Classroom Routines and Ten-Minute Math activities, see *Implementing Investigations in Grade 3*.	• **All sessions**
Student Activity Book	**Daily Practice** pages in the *Student Activity Book* provide one of three types of written practice: **reinforcement** of the content of the unit, **ongoing review,** or **enrichment** opportunities. Some Daily Practice pages will also have Ongoing Review items with multiple-choice problems similar to those on standardized tests.	• **All sessions**
	Homework pages in the *Student Activity Book* are an extension of the work done in class. At times they help students prepare for upcoming activities.	• **Session 1.1** • **Session 2.6** • **Session 1.2** • **Session 3.2** • **Session 1.4** • **Session 3.3** • **Session 2.2** • **Session 3.5** • **Session 2.4**
Student Math Handbook	**Math Words and Ideas** in the *Student Math Handbook* are pages that summarize key words and ideas. Most Words and Ideas pages have at least one exercise.	• **Student Math Handbook, pp. 105–117, 120–123**
	Games pages are found in a section of the *Student Math Handbook*.	• **No games are introduced in this unit.**

Supporting the Range of Learners

Sessions	1.1	1.2	1.3	1.4	1.5	2.2	2.3	2.4	2.6	3.1	3.2	3.3	3.4
Intervention		•	•	•				•		•	•		•
Extension	•				•	•	•	•		•		•	
ELL	•				•			•	•				•

Intervention

Suggestions are made to support and engage students who are having difficulty with a particular idea, activity, or problem.

Extension

Suggestions are made to support and engage students who finish early or may be ready for additional challenge.

English Language Learners (ELL)

In this unit, students use both U.S. standard and metric units to measure length. Some English Language Learners may have experience with metric measurement that is not shared by their native English speaking peers, but may not have the English language vocabulary to explain what they are doing as they measure. You can help them by introducing the English terms for the metric measurements (meter, centimeter, etc.), so that they may serve as role models to their native English-speaking classmates. If possible, pair a student experienced with the metric system with a student experienced with U.S. standard measures during work in this unit.

As students work through the material in this unit, they will encounter vocabulary about 2-D shapes and measurement that may be new to them. You can help English Language Learners master this vocabulary by using it in the context of various activities and by providing consistent visual supports.

The Math Words and Ideas pages in the *Student Math Handbook* can be a particularly useful reference for the English Language Learners in your classroom. When helpful, students can also create their own word banks to include native language translations or additional vocabulary not included in the Math Words and Ideas pages. Students can add to these word banks throughout the unit.

In the assessment activities in this unit, some English Language Learners may not be ready to independently write explanations of their work. Ask guided questions to help them. If necessary, provide other means for them to answer questions, such as drawings or diagrams (when appropriate), writing in their native language (if permitted by your school or district), or transcribing their words for them.

Working with the Range of Learners: Classroom Cases is a set of episodes written by teachers that focuses on meeting the needs of the range of learners in the classroom. In the first section, *Setting up the Mathematical Community,* teachers write about how they create a supportive and productive learning environment in their classrooms. In the next section, *Accommodations for Learning,* teachers focus on specific modifications they make to meet the needs of some of their learners. In the last section, *Language and Representation,* teachers share how they help students use representations and develop language to investigate and express mathematical ideas. The questions at the end of each case provide a starting point for your own reflection or for discussion with colleagues. See *Implementing Investigations in Grade 3* for this set of episodes.

INVESTIGATION 1

Mathematical Emphases

Linear Measurement Measuring with standard units

Math Focus Points

◆ Reviewing the length of units of measure (inch, foot, yard, centimeter, and meter)

◆ Establishing measurement benchmarks

◆ Using U.S. standard and metric units to accurately measure length

◆ Recognizing and explaining possible sources of measurement error

Linear Measurement Understanding and finding perimeter

Math Focus Points

◆ Understanding perimeter as the measure around the outside edges of a 2-dimensional figure

◆ Finding perimeter using standard units

◆ Creating different shapes with the same perimeter

◆ Finding the perimeter of an irregular shape

Linear Measurement

	Student Activity Book	Student Math Handbook	Professional Development: Read Ahead of Time	
SESSION 1.1 p. 22				
Using U.S. and Metric Units to Measure Length Students identify U.S. standard and metric measurement units (centimeter, meter, inch, foot, yard) and the tools used to measure these units. To practice measuring and establish measurement benchmarks, they find and measure objects in the classroom that are approximately the length of each of these units.	1–4	104, 105, 106, 107, 108	• **Mathematics in This Unit,** p. 10 • **Teacher Note:** Metric and U.S. Standard Units of Measure, p. 137 • **Part 4: Ten-Minute Math** in *Implementing Investigations in Grade 3:* Practicing Place Value	
SESSION 1.2 p. 29				
Introducing Perimeter Students establish an understanding of perimeter. They use U.S. standard and metric units to measure the perimeters of shapes and the 2-D faces of objects in the classroom.	5–8	110–111, 112–113		
SESSION 1.3 p. 37				
Assessment: Measuring Perimeter Students discuss common measurement errors and ways to avoid them. In Math Workshop they solve story problems about perimeter and are assessed as they measure the perimeter of a large shape mapped out in the classroom.	5–6, 9–11	108, 110–111, 112–113	• **Teacher Note:** Making Careful Measurements, p. 138; Introducing and Managing the *LogoPaths* Software, p. 139; About the Mathematics in the *LogoPaths* Software, p. 142	
SESSION 1.4 p. 45				
Perimeter Problems Students discuss why different shapes can have the same perimeter. In Math Workshop, they continue the previous session's activities. They also put in order a set of shapes by perimeter and work on an optional *LogoPaths* activity that involves using steps and 90-degree turns to complete drawings of incomplete rectangles.	9–10, 12–16	110–111, 112–113		
SESSION 1.5 p. 50				
Ordering Shapes by Perimeter Students compare the perimeters of shapes with different numbers of sides. They continue unfinished Math Workshop activities about perimeter from Sessions 3 and 4 and are introduced to the Ten-Minute Math, *Quick Images: 2-D.*	9–10, 12–13, 17	110–111, 112–113	• **Part 4: Ten-Minute Math** in *Implementing Investigations in Grade 3:* Quick Images	

Classroom Routines and Ten-Minute Math

See page 16 for an overview.

What's the Temperature?	Temperature graph in the classroom.
• Mount the thermometer outside the classroom window.	***Practicing Place Value***
	• **No materials needed**
• Post the date and temperature chart and the	

Materials to Gather	Materials to Prepare
• **Inch/centimeter ruler; yardstick; meterstick** (one per student) • **Adding machine tape** (available as needed)	• **M7–M8, Family Letter** Make copies. (1 per student) • **Chart paper** Label the chart paper "Measurement Tools." Label the subheads "U.S. Standard" and "Metric." • **Chart paper** Label the chart paper "Measurement Benchmarks." Label the subheads "Centimeter," "Inch," "Foot," "Yard," and "Meter."
• **$8\frac{1}{2}''$ x 11″ paper** (1 per student) • **Inch/centimeter rulers** (1 per student) • **Yardsticks/metersticks** (1 per pair) • **Adding machine tape** (available as needed)	• **M9–M10, Family Letter** Make copies. (1 per student)
• **Inch/centimeter rulers** (1 per student or pair) • **Yardsticks/metersticks** (1 per pair) • **Computers with** *LogoPaths* **software installed**	• **M1–M3,** *LogoPaths: Missing Measures* Make copies. (1 per student) (optional) • **M14, Assessment Checklist: Measuring Perimeter** Make copies. (1 per 6 students) ☑ • **M15, Assessment: Measuring Perimeter** Make copies. (1 per student) • **Chart paper** Label the chart paper "Measurement Guidelines." • **Measuring Perimeter** Use masking tape to map out a nonrectangular perimeter in your classroom for the students to measure. You can use walls as part of the perimeter or map out a perimeter on the floor if you have a large enough open area.
• **M14,** See Session 1.3. • **M15, Assessment: Measuring Perimeter** (from Session 1.3) • **Inch/centimeter rulers** (1 per pair) • **String or adding machine tape** (available as needed) • **Yardsticks/metersticks** (1 per pair) • **Computers with** *LogoPaths* **software installed**	• **M1–M3,** *LogoPaths: Missing Measures* Make copies. (1 per student) (optional)
• **M14,** See Session 1.3. • **M15, Assessment: Measuring Perimeter** (from Session 1.3) • **Inch/centimeter rulers** (1 per student) • **Yardsticks/metersticks** (1 per pair) • **Computers with** *LogoPaths* **software installed**	• **M1–M3,** *LogoPaths: Missing Measures* Make copies. (1 per student) (optional) • **T52–T54,** *Quick Images: 2-D* 🖵 Cut apart and set aside Images 1 and 2 for this session. Store cut-apart transparencies for future use.

🖵 Overhead Transparency   ☑ Checklist available

Using U.S. and Metric Units to Measure Length

Math Focus Points

◆ Reviewing the length of units of measure (inch, foot, yard, centimeter, and meter)

◆ Establishing measurement benchmarks

Vocabulary

measurement benchmark

Today's Plan		Materials
① ACTIVITY **Measurement Tools and Standard Units**	🕐 15 MIN · CLASS	• Inch/centimeter ruler, yardstick, meterstick; Chart: "Measurement Tools"*
② ACTIVITY **Estimating and Measuring Lengths**	🕐 25 MIN · PAIRS	• *Student Activity Book,* p. 1 • Inch/centimeter rulers; yardstick/meterstick
③ DISCUSSION **Measurement Benchmarks**	🕐 20 MIN · CLASS	• *Student Activity Book,* p. 1 • Chart: "Measurement Benchmarks"*; adding machine tape
④ SESSION FOLLOW-UP **Daily Practice and Homework**		• *Student Activity Book,* pp. 2–4 • *Student Math Handbook,* pp. 104, 105, 106, 107, 108 • M7–M8, Family Letter*

*See *Materials to Prepare,* p. 21.

Ten-Minute Math

Practicing Place Value Say "one hundred twenty-three," and have students write the number. Make sure all students can read, write, and say this number correctly. Ask students to solve these problems mentally, if possible:

• What is 123 + 20? 123 + 40? 123 + 60? 123 + 200? 123 + 400? 123 + 600?

Write each answer on the board. Ask students to compare each sum with 123. Which places have the same digits? Which do not? Why?

If time remains, pose additional similar problems using these numbers: 261 and 198.

ACTIVITY

Measurement Tools and Standard Units

15 MIN   CLASS

For the next few weeks we will be working on 2-D geometry and measurement. To start, let's think about different parts of things that can be measured, different ways to measure, and different tools we can use to measure.

Direct the students' attention to a window in your classroom. If you have no window, pick another object that can be measured.

Look at that window in our classroom. If I asked, "How big is this window?," what would you measure in order to answer this question?

The purpose of this question is to allow students to notice different aspects of a shape or object that can be measured. For example, they may point out that you could measure how tall or wide (length or width) the window is, how much space the glass covers (area), how thick it is (depth), how much it weighs, how long it is around the edge (perimeter), and so on. As each aspect is mentioned, provide the correct measurement term (height, area, etc.). Point out to the students that different measurements of an object might be useful in different ways. For example, you would need to know the area to find a shade to cover the whole window, the perimeter to put trim around the outside, etc.

Direct the students' attention to the "Measurement Tools" chart you prepared. Then show the students a ruler, yardstick, and meterstick.

For the next few days we will be measuring length using these tools. Who remembers which tools we used when we studied data? What do we call these tools and the units they measure? Where should I write them on this chart?❶

As students name each U.S. standard measurement tool, ask them what units each tool measures, how long each tool is, what smaller units are included in each tool, and how many of these units there are. Record this information on the chart.

In the data unit, we used U.S. standard units to measure. Which of these tools measures metric units? What are the names of the units they measure?

❷ **English Language Learners** You may want to preview this activity with English Language Learners prior to the session. Since many English Language Learners will be familiar with the metric measurement system, begin by encouraging them to demonstrate measuring using metric tools and metric terms. Then review the U. S. standard measurement tools and units students used in survey and line plots. Have students repeat each term after you. Then encourage them to say the terms on their own. You may want to pair English Language Learners with native speakers so they can assist each other with the U. S. standard and metric measurements.

Repeat the same procedure for the metric tools, once again recording the information on the chart. Students are likely to be less familiar with metric measurement and may not know the number of centimeters in a meter. Connecting the number of **cents** (pennies) in a dollar to the number of **cent**imeters in a meter is a helpful way for students to remember this relationship.❷

Measurement Tools

U.S. Standard		Metric	
Tool	Units	Tool	Units
Ruler	Foot 12 Inches	Ruler	Centimeters
Yardstick	Yard 3 Feet 36 Inches	Meterstick	Meter 100 Centimeters

Students name U.S. standard and metric measuring tools and the units each tool measures.

ACTIVITY

25 MIN   PAIRS

② Estimating and Measuring Lengths

Explain that for the remainder of this math session, students will work on a measurement activity in which they first use estimation to find objects that are about the same size as each unit of measure—inch, foot, yard, centimeter, and meter. They then measure each object to determine the accuracy of their estimates.

Before you begin to measure, use your eyes to find objects that you think are the size of each unit. For example, if you plan to start by finding things that are about an inch long, look around the room for things to measure that you estimate *are that size. Find and measure a few objects for each unit before you move on to the next unit of measure. That will help you get really good at remembering about how long each unit is and estimating the length of things.* ❸

Make sure that students understand that the objects they record do not have to be *exactly* the length they are looking for, but should be close enough to help them develop a good sense of each unit.

When you find things close *to a centimeter long, record them on your paper. Then do the same for an inch, a foot, and so on. You don't need to write the actual measurements, just the names of the objects. If your estimates aren't close to the units of measure, don't record those objects, only the ones that are close.*

As students find objects for each unit, they record them on *Student Activity Book* page 1.

Students measure objects in the classroom to get a sense of the size of each unit of measure.

Math Note

❸ Distinguishing Between Yards and Meters
Since yards and meters are very close in length, students are not expected to be able to visually distinguish between these two units of measure without the use of a measuring tool. As they develop a sense of the length of a yard or a meter, students can begin to understand that a meter is slightly longer than a yard. The distinction between yards and meters becomes more important as students work with longer measures in future grades and later in life (a 100 meter race is almost $9\frac{1}{2}$ meters longer than a 100 yard race).

Name _____ Date _____
Perimeter, Angles, and Area

Finding Lengths
Use a ruler, yardstick, and meterstick to find objects that are about the same length as these measurement units. Record the objects that you find for each unit.

Centimeter	Inch
Example: The tip of my pencil	

Foot	Yard/Meter

Session 1.1   Unit 4 ①

▲ **Student Activity Book, p. 1**

ONGOING ASSESSMENT: Observing Students at Work

Students use estimation to find and measure objects close to the following lengths: one inch, one foot, one yard, one centimeter, and one meter.

- **Are students using the measurement tools accurately?** Do they know how to line up a ruler to measure an object that is approximately a centimeter or an inch long? A yardstick to measure an object that is approximately a foot long?

- **Are they making reasonable estimates for each unit of measure?** For example, if they are looking for lengths equal to a yard, do they measure objects that are close to a yard?

DIFFERENTIATION: Supporting the Range of Learners

Extension If some students work through *Student Activity Book* page 1 quickly and are clearly familiar with the measurement tools, ask them to find some lengths of multiple units such as five feet, six inches, ten meters, and so on.

DISCUSSION

20 MIN CLASS

3 Measurement Benchmarks

Math Focus Points for Discussion

◆ Establishing measurement benchmarks

Call the class together to share the objects they found for each unit of measure.

Having pictures in your mind of things that are about as long as a centimeter, an inch, a foot, a yard, and a meter can help you get a sense of how long each unit of measure is. We can call the objects that we picture **measurement benchmarks**.

Let's share some of the objects you found that were close to each unit. They don't have to be exactly right, but close enough so you have a picture of how long each unit is. Let's start with centimeters, since they are the smallest of these units. What objects did you find that were close to, or exactly one centimeter?

As students share their findings, record them on the Measurement Benchmarks chart you prepared. Ask questions to help students communicate clearly about what part of each object they measured. Model the use of measurement terms, like length, width, height, etc. For example:

[Pilar], you said that the light switch is about one centimeter. What part of the light switch did you measure? . . . So you measured the *width,* or how wide it is.

Ask some questions specifically about yards and meters.

What did you notice about yards and meters when you looked for objects that were about a yard long and about a meter long? Did you use some of the same objects for both units? Did you find different objects? Which unit is longer, a yard or a meter?

Continue to encourage students to use appropriate vocabulary to describe what they measured. Collect and record a few responses for each unit of measure. A completed chart might appear as follows:

Measurement Benchmarks	
Centimeter	**Inch**
Edge of a centimeter cube	Edge of an inch cube
Width of the light switch	Width of color tile
	Thickness of social studies book
Foot	**Yard**
Width of construction paper	Width of the window
Length of teacher's reading book	
Meter	
Distance from the floor to the white board	

Measurement benchmarks can help you when you need to figure out about how long something is when you don't have a measurement tool. Using these benchmarks can help you estimate measurements. For example, what if I asked you to cut a piece of this adding machine tape four feet long and you didn't have a ruler or yardstick. Is there anything about a foot long on our list of measurement benchmarks that you could use instead of a ruler?

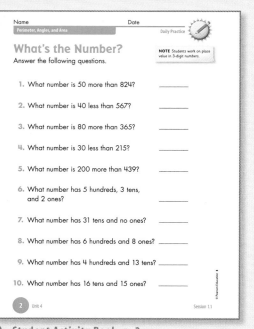

▲ Student Activity Book, p. 2

Take two or three suggestions, and ask a couple of students to demonstrate how they could use one of the benchmarks to estimate and cut four feet of tape.

If students pick a benchmark that is not exactly a foot long, ask questions to help them consider whether they need a little more or a little less than four lengths of that benchmark. For example:

I see you chose a reading book to use as a benchmark for one foot and measured four lengths of the book. Is the book a little more or a little less than a foot? Do you need more or less tape to have exactly four feet?

SESSION FOLLOW-UP
4 Daily Practice and Homework

 Daily Practice: For ongoing review, have students complete *Student Activity Book* page 2.

 Homework: Students consider a variety of measurement scenarios and choose an appropriate tool and unit of measure for each one on *Student Activity Book* pages 3–4.

 Student Math Handbook: Students and families may use *Student Math Handbook* pages 104, 105, 106, 107, 108 for reference and review. See pages 160–164 in the back of this unit.

 Family Letter: Send home copies of the Family Letter (M7–M8).

▲ Student Activity Book, p. 3

▲ Student Activity Book, p. 4

Introducing Perimeter

Math Focus Points

- Understanding perimeter as the measure around the outside edges of a 2-dimensional figure
- Finding perimeter using standard units
- Using U.S. standard and metric units to accurately measure length

Vocabulary

perimeter

Today's Plan			Materials
ACTIVITY **① An Ant's Path**	20 MIN	PAIRS	• $8\frac{1}{2}$" x 11" paper; inch/centimeter rulers
DISCUSSION **② Comparing Strategies and Results**	15 MIN	CLASS	
ACTIVITY **③ Finding and Measuring Perimeters**	25 MIN	PAIRS	• *Student Activity Book,* pp. 5–6 • Inch/centimeter rulers; yardsticks/metersticks; adding machine tape (available as needed)
SESSION FOLLOW-UP **④ Daily Practice and Homework**			• *Student Activity Book,* pp. 7–8 • *Student Math Handbook,* pp. 110–111, 112–113 • M9–M10, Family Letter*

*See *Materials to Prepare,* p. 21.

Ten-Minute Math

Practicing Place Value Write 356 on the board and have students practice saying it to a partner. Make sure all students can read, write and say this number correctly.

Ask students:

- Find and sketch 5–6 different ways to make 356 using only strips of 10 and single stickers (such as, 35 strips and 6 singles or 25 strips and 106 singles).

Collect a few examples on the board and ask students how they found their answers.

Did anyone notice a pattern?

20 MIN   PAIRS

ACTIVITY

1 An Ant's Path

In our last math class, we talked about the parts of a window [or whatever object you discussed in Session 1] that could be measured. Someone mentioned that we could measure around the outside edge of the window. [Trace around the outside edge.] Does anyone know what that measure is called?

Establish that the measure around the outside edge of a 2-dimensional shape is called the perimeter.

Hold up an $8\frac{1}{2}''$ x 11″ piece of paper.

Imagine that an ant started in this corner (choose any corner) and walked all the way around the edge of the paper until she got back to where she started. [Follow this path with your finger.] Your job is to work in pairs to find out how far this ant would have to walk to get all the way around the perimeter of this paper, in other words, to walk all the way around and end up just where she started. How could you figure this out?

Ask two or three students to explain what tools and measurement units they will use to determine how far the ant will walk. If no one mentions measuring in centimeters, bring it up yourself.

[Keisha] and [Philip] both talked about using the ruler to measure the number of inches the ant will travel around the perimeter of the paper. Look at your rulers. What other unit of measurement could you use?

Suggest that students measure first with inches and, if time allows, measure the perimeter a second time with centimeters.

Make sure it is clear to everyone that the task is to find the length of the outside edge of the paper. Then distribute one $8\frac{1}{2}''$ x 11″ sheet of paper to each student.

Students measure the number of inches an ant would have to travel around the perimeter of the paper.

ONGOING ASSESSMENT: Observing Students at Work

Students use inches, centimeters, or both to measure the perimeter of an $8\frac{1}{2}''$ x 11″ sheet of paper.

- **Do students choose an appropriate tool for measuring the perimeter of the paper?** Are their measurements of each side accurate?

- **Do students know to add up all of the measurements of the sides to find the total perimeter?** Are they able to add the half inches?

DIFFERENTIATION: Supporting the Range of Learners

Intervention If students are having difficulty getting started, ask questions such as:

- Where is your ant going to start? Where will it end up? Can you trace the path of the ant with your finger? What part of the path can you measure first? How can you make sure you are measuring accurately?

For some students, the difficulty of this task is in manipulating the ruler so that it lies along the edge of the paper. Demonstrate how one student can hold the ruler while the other reads the measurement. If reading the tools accurately is difficult, show them on one edge how to read it and allow them to do the rest.

DISCUSSION

② Comparing Strategies and Results

15 MIN CLASS

Math Focus Points for Discussion

◆ Finding perimeter using standard units

Hold up an $8\frac{1}{2}$″ x 11″ sheet of paper used by one of your students.

How did you find the perimeter of this piece of paper? In other words, how far would the ant have to walk to start at one corner and walk all of the way around the edge of the paper?

Begin by asking three or four students to explain how they found the total measurement of the perimeter of the paper. This may involve explaining which tool they used to measure each side of the paper and then how they added up each length at the end. Some students may notice that the rectangular shape of paper has two sets of equal sides so once they measure sides A and B ($8\frac{1}{2}$ + 11) they can add them again to find the total of all the lengths.

Students might say:

"I measured the top and got $8\frac{1}{2}$ inches. Then I measured one side and got 11 inches. I knew the opposite sides were the same, so I didn't need to measure them. I just added each number ($8\frac{1}{2}$ and 11) twice to get my answer."

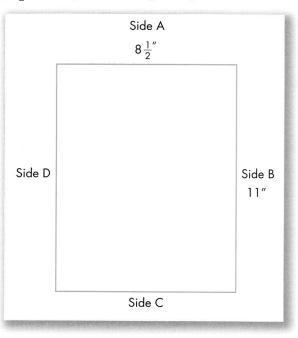

Side A
$8\frac{1}{2}$″

Side D

Side B
11″

Side C

Sometimes when we measure perimeter, we forget that we're measuring how long something is, since our measurement ends at the same place that it started. In other words, if the ant walked around the perimeter of this paper, it would have started at one corner, walked all the way around, and ended up at the same corner. Let's stretch out the perimeter of the paper into one straight line.

[Keisha], what was the first distance the ant would have walked when it started from this corner? [Point to a connected vertex.] Can you draw a horizontal line on the board that shows that distance?

Continue asking volunteers for the measure of each edge of the paper, and have them draw the length on the board until you have a line that is 39 inches long. Have students mark the end of each measure, as in the diagram below. If time allows, have students draw a second line, this time showing the strategy of measuring only Sides A and B and then adding them again by drawing the sets of parallel sides first ($8\frac{1}{2}$ inches, $8\frac{1}{2}$ inches, 11 inches, and 11 inches).

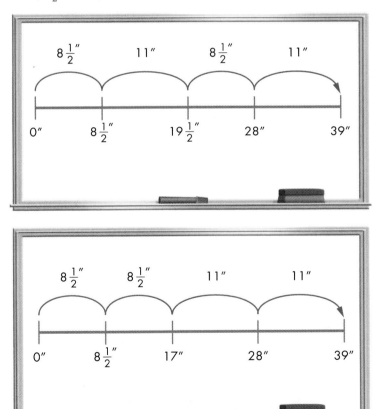

The perimeter in inches is 39. Some of you also measured the perimeter in centimeters. What was your answer? Why is the answer in centimeters different than the answer in inches?

Math Notes

❶ **The Smaller the Unit, the Higher the Count** In Grade 2, students discovered that when measuring any length, the smaller the unit of measure, the higher the count (and vice versa). For example, when measuring the perimeter of the paper in the activity, the count in inches is 39 while the count in centimeters is approximately 97.5. Raise this idea as students measure, questioning them about how their measurements would change if they used inches instead of feet or feet instead of yards. Students will explore this idea further in Grade 4 in the context of linear measure and as they measure with square and cubic units.

❷ **Finding Perimeters of 3-D Objects** Students may readily identify perimeter on 2-D objects in the classroom, such as the perimeter of a world map or the perimeter of a piece of construction paper. However, measuring the perimeter of 3-D objects presents more of a challenge since students must first identify a 2-dimensional component of these objects. It is important for students to understand that perimeter is a measurement of a 2-dimensional object. Therefore, when they measure the perimeter on a 3-dimensional object, they are actually measuring the perimeter of one face (surface) of that object—for example the distance around the front surface of the door, the top face of the table, the face of the whiteboard, etc. Perimeter is a linear measure; that is, it is measured in inches or centimeters or feet, etc.

Teaching Note

❸ **Measuring the Length of Curved Sides** As students measure the perimeter of objects in the classroom, they are likely to encounter objects with some or all curved sides. Allow students to consider ways to measure these curved edges. They may attempt to move a ruler in small increments in an effort to estimate the distance. Ask questions that encourage them to think about the accuracy of this strategy. Other students may come up with the idea of using the adding machine tape (or another flexible material such as string or masking tape), wrapping it around the curved section, and then measuring the tape or string when it is stretched out.

Most students should recognize that since an inch is a bigger unit than a centimeter, it takes fewer inches to measure the same length. Students will continue to develop this understanding as they use different units of measure during the rest of this investigation. ❶

ACTIVITY

③ Finding and Measuring Perimeters

25 MIN **PAIRS**

Look around the classroom at all of the objects and shapes around us. Imagine an ant taking a walk around a perimeter that you see. Remember that the perimeter is the length of the outside edge of a shape. What objects or parts of objects do you see that have perimeters you can measure? ❷ ❸

Elicit and list a few ideas to ensure that all students are clear on the directions for the activity. As ideas are shared, ask a volunteer to trace the perimeter of each suggested object. For example:

[Oscar] suggested measuring the perimeter of the 100 Chart. [Gina], can you trace the perimeter so that everyone can see what will be measured?

[Nancy] suggested measuring a perimeter of the box that holds the connecting cubes. [Nancy], can you trace with your finger what you will measure? . . . What perimeter did she trace? [the perimeter of one side face of the box] . . . Can someone trace a different perimeter of the box that could be measured? What could we say that is? [the perimeter of the top face of the box]

A student traces the perimeter of the top face of a box.

Choose a perimeter that all students will measure in the activity that follows. Make sure this perimeter is fairly large, such as the perimeter of the whiteboard or a bulletin board. Ask students to write the name of this object in the first column on *Student Activity Book* page 5. Students will compare their results for this perimeter at the beginning of the next session, with a focus on identifying and explaining measurement errors.

For the rest of this session, students work with partners to measure the assigned perimeter and other perimeters of their choosing. Let them know that in addition to rulers and yardsticks/metersticks, adding machine tape is also available for their use. Students record their measurements on *Student Activity Book* pages 5–6.

ONGOING ASSESSMENT: Observing Students at Work

Students measure the perimeter of objects in the classroom.

- **Can students identify the perimeter of an object?**

- **Can they use measurement tools to accurately measure its perimeter?**

- **Do they measure each side of a rectangle or recognize that they need to measure only one length and width?**

- **What strategies do students use to measure the perimeters of objects with curved sides?** Do they estimate the lengths of these sides? Do they realize that they can use something flexible, like adding machine tape or string, which can be marked at the beginning and end of the length and then measured?

▲ Student Activity Book, p. 5

▲ Student Activity Book, p. 6

Teaching Note

❹ Using Alternate Measuring Materials If students do not have measuring tools at home, suggest they use string, yarn, or rope to measure the perimeters. These lengths can be brought to school and measured before the next math class.

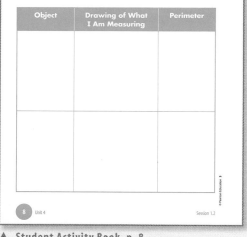

▲ Student Activity Book, p. 7

▲ Student Activity Book, p. 8

DIFFERENTIATION: Supporting the Range of Learners

Intervention Talk to students about how to measure accurately as they are working. Be alert for issues such as: measuring from the wrong end of the ruler or yardstick/meterstick, not lining up the end of the tool with the end of the distance, and leaving gaps when moving a tool to measure distances longer than that tool. Encourage students to consider why they need to pay attention to these issues. For example:

- I noticed that this is where your last measurement ended [place finger on that spot], but when you moved the yardstick, you started again here [place finger there]. What about the part in between? Aren't you going to measure that? How can you be sure that you measure the whole distance?

SESSION FOLLOW-UP

❹ Daily Practice and Homework

 Daily Practice: For ongoing review, have students complete *Student Activity Book* page 7.

 Homework: Students find and measure the perimeter of two or three objects at home. They record their findings on *Student Activity Book* page 8.❹

 Student Math Handbook: Students and families may use *Student Math Handbook* pages 110–111, 112–113 for reference and review. See pages 160–164 in the back of this unit.

Family Letter: Send home copies of the Family Letter (M9–M10).

Assessment: Measuring Perimeter

Math Focus Points

❖ Recognizing and explaining possible sources of measurement error

❖ Finding perimeter using standard units

❖ Creating different shapes with the same perimeter

Today's Plan		Materials
DISCUSSION **① Why Are Our Measurements Different?**	15 MIN CLASS	• *Student Activity Book,* pp. 5–6 (from Session 1.2) • Inch/centimeter rulers; yardsticks/ metersticks; Chart: "Measurement Guidelines"*
MATH WORKSHOP **② Perimeter Problems** **2A Perimeter Problems** **2B Assessment: Measuring Perimeter**	45 MIN	**2A** • *Student Activity Book,* pp. 9–10 • Inch/centimeter rulers; yardsticks/ metersticks **2B** • M14*; M15* • Inch/centimeter rulers; yardsticks/ metersticks; masking tape*
ACTIVITY **③ Introducing *LogoPaths: Missing Measures* (optional)**	CLASS GROUPS	• M1–M3* • Computers with *LogoPaths* software installed
SESSION FOLLOW-UP **④ Daily Practice**		• *Student Activity Book,* p. 11 • *Student Math Handbook,* pp. 108, 110–111, 112–113

*See *Materials to Prepare,* p. 21.

Ten-Minute Math

Practicing Place Value Say, "four hundred thirty-seven," and ask students to write the number. Make sure all students can read, write, and say this number correctly. Ask students to solve these problems mentally, if possible:

- What is 437 + 30? 437 − 30? 437 + 50? 437 − 100? 437 + 200? 437 − 200? Which places have the same digits? Which do not? Why?

Write each answer on the board. Ask students to compare each sum or difference with 437. If time remains, pose additional similar problems with these numbers: 384 and 506.

Teaching Note

① **Measurement Errors** Students may report identical measurements differently if some are using feet and inches, while others are using only inches. These differences can distract students from seeing measurement errors, the focus of this discussion. If some students reported the length in feet and inches and others used all inches, work briefly to convert all measurements to one or the other. Then focus on why some measurements differ even though they are expressed in the same units.

DISCUSSION

1 Why Are Our Measurements Different?

15 MIN CLASS

Math Focus Points for Discussion

◆ Recognizing and explaining possible sources of measurement error

In the last math class, everyone measured the perimeter of the whiteboard (or whatever object you selected). While you were measuring, I noticed that not everyone was getting the same answer, even if you were using the same units of measure. Who measured in feet and inches? What answers did you get? Did anyone measure in meters and centimeters? What answers did you get?

List student responses on the board, grouping them by units of measure.

Look at the list of answers for feet and inches. Is it possible to have more than one correct answer? . . . Why do you think there are different answers on this list?**①**

Students might say:

"We had a hard time remembering where we left off when we moved the ruler to measure the next foot, so I think we might have left some spaces that we didn't measure."

"Sometimes the ruler slipped when we were measuring, so that might have messed up our answer."

"We got mixed up when we were adding all the sides, so I think we may have made an adding mistake."

You have just shared some of the problems that you had measuring the perimeter of the board. Let's make a list of some things to remember that can help you measure accurately. We can call them our Measurement Guidelines. What are some things we should put on this list?❷

Measurement Guidelines

Line up the end of the ruler (yardstick/meterstick) with the edge of the object and hold it steady

Avoid gaps or overlaps by marking the end point of each measure before moving the measuring tool

Write down partial measurements in order to keep track

Measure twice to double-check

Double-check computation

Let the students know that even people very experienced with measuring follow guidelines like these. Carpenters, for example, are known for their motto, "Measure twice, cut once," since they always double-check each measurement to make sure they do not have to re-cut the wood to correct a measurement mistake.

Keep the Measurement Guidelines chart posted for the rest of this investigation.

MATH WORKSHOP

❷ Perimeter Problems

45 MIN

In this Math Workshop, students work on two activities to continue developing their understanding of perimeter and their accuracy using measurement tools. They work in pairs on *Student Activity Book* pages 9–10. Make sure all students complete Problem 2 (Pilar's Yard) during this session since this problem will be discussed at the start of the next session.

Professional Development

❷ **Teacher Note:** Making Careful Measurements, p. 138

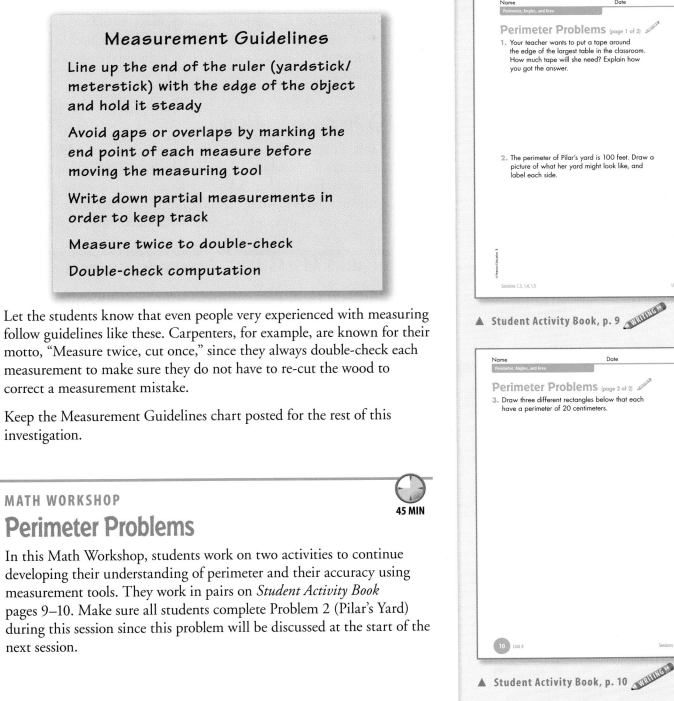

▲ Student Activity Book, p. 9

▲ Student Activity Book, p. 10

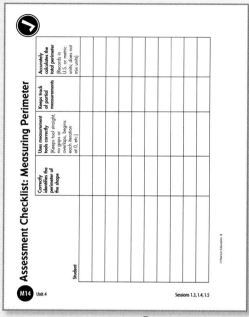

▲ **Resource Masters, M14** ✓

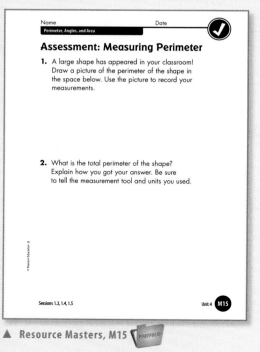

▲ **Resource Masters, M15**

In addition, students work in groups of three to measure the perimeter of the large shape you mapped out in the classroom. Have them record their measurements on Assessment: Measuring Perimeter (M15). Two groups of three can work on this activity at the same time if they start at different points on the perimeter.

During this and the next two sessions, observe students as they measure the perimeter of the large shape. Use Assessment Checklist: Measuring Perimeter (M14) to keep track of how individual students are doing on this task.

2A Perimeter Problems

PAIRS

In this activity, students solve three problems, one in which they measure the perimeter of a table and two in which they create shapes with given perimeters. For Problem 3, some students may choose to use their centimeter rulers to draw the three rectangles with perimeters equaling 20 centimeters, although they are not required to do so.

ONGOING ASSESSMENT: Observing Students at Work

Students measure perimeter and create shapes with given perimeters.❸

- **Can students accurately measure the perimeter of the large table?**

- **Can students create multiple shapes from a given perimeter?**

DIFFERENTIATION: Supporting the Range of Learners

Intervention Some students may be unclear about how to create a shape from a given perimeter. Help these students by providing one side of Pilar's yard. Then ask questions like the following:

- I just drew one side of Pilar's yard that's 20 feet (or whatever length you chose) long. How much of the 100 ft. perimeter is left? Can you draw a second side? How long is your side? How much of the perimeter is left now?

Students who are having difficulty creating three different rectangles with a perimeter of 20 centimeters may have a better understanding of the possibilities after the discussion of Pilar's yard at the start of the next session. Let them know that they can return to this problem during the next session's Math Workshop.

2B Assessment: Measuring Perimeter

Let the students know that they will work in groups of three to measure the perimeter of the nonrectangular figure mapped out on a section of the classroom floor (or the floor of whatever place you choose). Remind them to refer to the Measurement Guidelines they generated at the beginning of the session as they work on this activity.

Students measure the perimeter of a nonrectangular figure.

ONGOING ASSESSMENT: Observing Students at Work

Students use U.S. standard or metric measurement units to measure the perimeter of a large nonrectangular shape.

- **What measurement tools/units do students use to measure the perimeter of this shape?**

- **Do students use the measurement guidelines to accurately measure the perimeter?** Do they keep their tools straight, remember what they have already measured, line up their tools without any gaps or overlaps, begin each iteration of their tool at zero, and so on?

- **Do students keep track of all the smaller measurements they make in order to accurately calculate the total?**

Professional Development

④ Teacher Note: Introducing and Managing the *LogoPaths* Software, p. 139

⑤ Teacher Note: About the Mathematics in the *LogoPaths* Software, p. 142

Technology Note

⑥ Working with the *LogoPaths* Software For a complete description and instructions about the *LogoPaths* software, see the *Software Support Reference Guide* contained on the CD in your curriculum unit package.

DIFFERENTIATION: Supporting the Range of Learners

Intervention This can be a difficult task for students who have trouble with organizing and keeping track of information. You can group a student who has these difficulties with classmates who are well organized.

ACTIVITY

CLASS   GROUPS

③ Introducing *LogoPaths: Missing Measures* (optional)

In this version of *Missing Measures,* students are given pictures of incomplete rectangles that include some dimensions. They use the *LogoPaths* software to draw and then complete each rectangle. This requires students to use forward (**FD**) and back (**BK**) commands and right (**RT**) and left (**LT**) turns of 90 degrees.④ ⑤ ⑥

I'm going to teach you a new *LogoPaths* activity called *Missing Measures.* The commands you use for this activity are like those you use when you play *Get the Toys*—forward and backward, and right and left turns of 90 degrees. The only difference is that the forward and backward commands don't have to be multiples of 10. In this activity, for example, it's possible to make forward and backward moves like 15 or 37.

To introduce the activity, draw the following figure on the board.

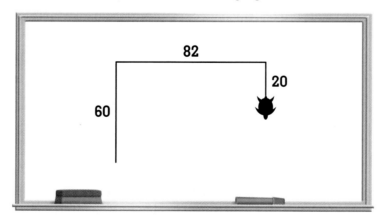

In *Missing Measures,* your job is to use the clues you see on incomplete rectangles like this one to write commands that will let the turtle finish each rectangle. First, you'll have to write commands to draw what's already shown and then the commands to finish the rectangle. What commands would you write to show what the turtle has drawn so far?

As students suggest commands, ask them to explain their suggestions. When the students reach a consensus, write the suggested commands next to the drawing on lines like those that appear on *LogoPaths: Missing Measures* (M1–M3).

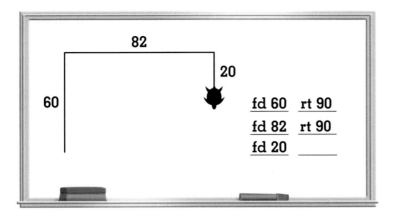

Open the *Free Explore* option in the *LogoPaths* software and enter the commands the class wrote. Use the Label Lengths tool  to check that the figure on the computer matches the one displayed. Keep the tool selected as you continue.

What commands should we type in now to help the turtle finish the rectangle?

Once again, as students suggest commands, ask them to explain their thinking.

Students might say:

 "I noticed that one side of the rectangle is 60 steps. The opposite side is only 20 steps so far, so it needs to be 40 steps more to make it equal to 60. The turtle needs to go forward 40 steps."

 "That side is finished, so now the turtle has to turn right 90 degrees to make the last side."

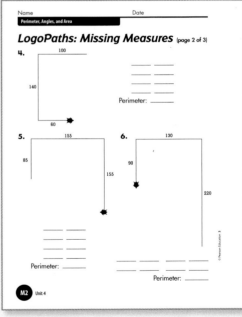

▲ Resource Masters, M1

▲ Resource Masters, M2

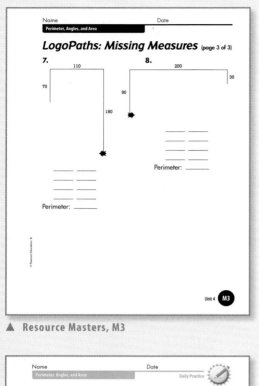

▲ Resource Masters, M3

▲ Student Activity Book, p. 11

After all of the new commands have been entered, use the **HT** command to hide the turtle so the students can see the full rectangle. Then use the Teach tool to make a procedure out of a set of commands in the Command Center. You will be asked to give it a name and the commands will be moved to the Teach Window in the proper format for a procedure. Let students know that their last task in this activity is to determine the perimeter of each rectangle they helped the turtle complete.

SESSION FOLLOW-UP
4 Daily Practice

Daily Practice: For reinforcement of this unit's content, have students complete *Student Activity Book* page 11.

Student Math Handbook: Students and families may use *Student Math Handbook* pages 108, 110–111, 112–113 for reference and review. See pages 160–164 in the back of this unit.

Perimeter Problems

Math Focus Points

◈ Creating different shapes with the same perimeter

◈ Finding perimeter using standard units

◈ Understanding perimeter as the measure around the outside edges of a 2-dimensional figure

Today's Plan		Materials
① DISCUSSION **Pilar's Yard**	🕐 👨‍👩‍👧 15 MIN CLASS	• *Student Activity Book,* pp. 9–10 (from Session 1. 3)
② MATH WORKSHOP **Perimeter Problems** **②A Ordering Shapes by Perimeter** **②B Perimeter Problems** **②C Assessment: Measuring Perimeter** **②D *LogoPaths* Activity: *Missing Measures* (optional)**	🕐 45 MIN	**②A** • *Student Activity Book,* pp. 12–13 • Inch/centimeter rulers; yardstick/ meterstick; string or adding machine tape **②B** • Materials from Session 1.3, p. 37 **②C** • Materials from Session 1.3, p. 37 **②D** • M1–M3* • Computers with *LogoPaths* software installed
③ SESSION FOLLOW-UP **Daily Practice and Homework**		• *Student Activity Book,* pp. 14–16 • *Student Math Handbook,* pp. 110–111, 112–113

*See *Materials to Prepare,* p. 21.

Ten-Minute Math

Practicing Place Value Write 538 on the board and have students practice saying it to a partner. Make sure all students can read, write, and say this number correctly.

Ask students:

• Find and sketch 5-6 different ways to make 538 using only strips of 10 and single stickers (such as, 53 strips and 8 singles or 52 strips and 18 singles).

Collect a few examples on the board and ask students how they found their answers.

Did anyone notice a pattern?

DISCUSSION

① Pilar's Yard

15 MIN   CLASS

Math Focus Points for Discussion

◆ Creating different shapes with the same perimeter

To prepare for this discussion, ask three or four students to put one of their drawings of Pilar's yard (Problem 2 on *Student Activity Book* page 9) on the board. They can tape or copy their drawings on the board. While some students may have drawn rectangles of various dimensions, include any non-rectangular shapes as well. If no student has drawn a nonrectangular shape with a perimeter of 100 feet, draw one yourself.

Students display their drawings of Pilar's yard.

What is the perimeter of all of these shapes? (Make sure everyone understands that the perimeter of each is 100 feet.) How can they look so different and still have the same perimeter?

Allow students a minute or two to talk to a partner about this question. Bring them back together and encourage a few students to explain.

Students might say:

"You can walk on different paths, but still take the same amount of steps."

"There's lots of different ways that you can make 100 with different numbers, so all you have to do is use those numbers for the length of the sides."

"If you stretched out all of these perimeters, they would all make lines 100 feet long."

Students who have time may wish to create other yards with perimeters of 100 feet during the Math Workshop that follows.

MATH WORKSHOP

45 MIN

② Perimeter Problems

Students return to the two Math Workshop activities from Session 1.3: Perimeter Problems and Measuring Perimeter. They are introduced to a new activity, Ordering Shapes by Perimeter, in which they look at four shapes and predict the order of their perimeters from shortest to longest. They then measure these shapes and re-record the order from shortest to longest. They also have the option of working during this session and the next on the *LogoPaths* activity, *Missing Measures*.

If students were in the middle of an activity at the end of the last session, ask them to complete that activity before choosing a new one.

②A Ordering Shapes by Perimeter

PAIRS

Students order the perimeters of four shapes from shortest to longest on *Student Activity Book* pages 12–13.

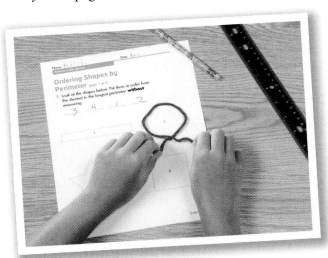

Students use strategies, such as measuring with string, to find the perimeter of the circle.

Name _____ Date _____

Perimeter, Angles, and Area

Ordering Shapes by Perimeter (page 1 of 2)

1. Look at the shapes below. Put them in order from the shortest to the longest perimeter **without** measuring.

_____ _____ _____ _____

A   B   C   D

12 Unit 4   Sessions 1.4, 1.5

▲ **Student Activity Book, p. 12**

Name _____ Date _____

Perimeter, Angles, and Area

Ordering Shapes by Perimeter (page 2 of 2)

2. Now choose a measurement tool and measure the perimeter of each shape. Put them in order from shortest to longest. Write the perimeter of each shape.

   Measurement tool you chose: _____

   _____ _____ _____ _____

3. Compare the lists you made before and after you measured. Did anything surprise you about the perimeters of these shapes? Explain what you found out.

Sessions 1.4, 1.5   Unit 4 13

▲ **Student Activity Book, p. 13**

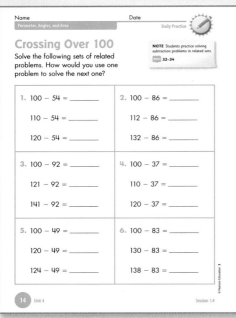

▲ **Student Activity Book, p. 14**

ONGOING ASSESSMENT: Observing Students at Work

Students predict the order of the perimeters of a set of shapes, then measure and compare the actual order to their predictions.

- **How accurately do students predict the order of the perimeters of the shapes from shortest to longest?** Do they consider the total length of the combined sides rather than the relative size of each figure to make their predictions?

- **Do students accurately measure the perimeter of each shape?** Do they have a strategy for measuring the perimeter of the circle?

- **Are they able to explain why their predictions of the order may differ from the actual order of the shapes by perimeter?**

DIFFERENTIATION: Supporting the Range of Learners

Intervention Some students may be unsure of how to measure the perimeter of the circle. Ask these students to consider how they can use the string or adding machine tape to find the length of the perimeter.

. . . .

2B Perimeter Problems

PAIRS

For details about this activity, see Session 1.3, page 40.

. . . .

2C Assessment: Measuring Perimeter

GROUPS

Continue to observe students, using Assessment Checklist: Measuring Perimeter (M14) to record your observations.

For details about this activity, see Session 1.3, page 41.

. . . .

2D *LogoPaths* Activity: *Missing Measures* (optional)

PAIRS INDIVIDUALS

Students work alone or with partners to solve the problems on *LogoPaths: Missing Measures* (M1–M3). Students are given pictures showing part of a rectangle and some of its dimensions and use *LogoPaths* commands to complete each rectangle. They then determine the perimeter of each.

ONGOING ASSESSMENT: Observing Students at Work

Students use *LogoPaths* commands, including steps and 90-degree turns, to create rectangles when they are given only parts of rectangles and some of their dimensions. They also determine the perimeter of the rectangles they create.

- **Can students use *LogoPaths* commands fluently?**

- **Do they use right and left turns consistently and accurately even when the turtle is not facing straight up?**

- **Are they able to determine the missing measures and turns from the given information (e.g., using the length of a side to determine the length of the parallel side)?**

- **Do they accurately determine the perimeter of each completed rectangle?**

SESSION FOLLOW-UP

3 Daily Practice and Homework

Daily Practice: For ongoing review, have students complete *Student Activity Book* page 14.

Homework: Students solve problems adding centimeters on *Student Activity Book* pages 15–16.

Student Math Handbook: Students and families may use *Student Math Handbook* pages 110–111, 112–113 for reference and review. See pages 160–164 in the back of this unit.

Name _____ Date _____
Perimeter, Angles, and Area   Homework

Frog Jumps (page 1 of 2)

NOTE Students practice adding and subtracting centimeters.
25, 106

Frog A   Frog B   Frog C   Frog D

Start   Finish
27 centimeters 34 centimeters 25 centimeters 28 centimeters

1. Frogs A, B, C, and D had a jumping relay race. How many centimeters did they jump altogether?

2. Did they jump more or less than one meter? Explain how you know.

Session 1.4   Unit 4   15

▲ Student Activity Book, p. 15

Name _____ Date _____
Perimeter, Angles, and Area   Homework

Frog Jumps (page 2 of 2)

Frog E   Frog F   Frog G   Frog H

Start   Finish
57 centimeters 65 centimeters 59 centimeters 60 centimeters

3. Frogs E, F, G, and H are bullfrogs. How many centimeters did they jump altogether?

4. How much farther did they jump than Frogs A, B, C, and D?

16   Unit 4   Session 1.4

▲ Student Activity Book, p. 16

Ordering Shapes by Perimeter

Math Focus Points

◆ Understanding perimeter as the measure around the outside edges of a 2-dimensional figure.

◆ Finding perimeter using standard units

◆ Creating different shapes with the same perimeter

Today's Plan		Materials
DISCUSSION ① **Ordering Shapes: What Did You Find?**	15 MIN CLASS	• *Student Activity Book,* pp. 12–13 (from Session 1.4) • Inch/centimeter rulers; yardsticks/metersticks
MATH WORKSHOP ② **Perimeter Problems** ②A Perimeter Problems ②B Assessment: Measuring Perimeter ②C Ordering Shapes by Perimeter ②D *LogoPaths* Activity: *Missing Measures* (optional)	30 MIN	②A • Materials from Session 1.3, p. 37 ②B • Materials from Session 1.3, p. 37 ②C • Materials from Session 1.4, p. 45 ②D • Materials from Session 1.4, p. 45
ACTIVITY ③ **Introducing *Quick Images: 2-D***	15 MIN CLASS	• T52*
SESSION FOLLOW-UP ④ **Daily Practice**		• *Student Activity Book,* p. 17 • *Student Math Handbook,* pp. 110–111, 112–113

*See *Materials to Prepare,* p. 21.

Ten-Minute Math

Practicing Place Value Say "six hundred thirty-seven," and ask students to write the number. Make sure all students can read, write, and say this number correctly. Ask students to solve these problems mentally, if possible:

• What is 637 + 40? 637 − 30? 637 + 60? 637 + 100? 637 + 300? 637 − 200?

Write each answer on the board. Ask students to compare each sum or difference with 637.

Which places have the same digits? Which do not? Why?

If time remains, pose additional similar problems using these numbers: 673 and 525.

DISCUSSION

① Ordering Shapes: What Did You Find?

15 MIN   CLASS

Math Focus Points for Discussion

◆ Understanding perimeter as the measure around the outside edges of a 2-dimensional figure

Call the students back together with their completed copies of *Student Activity Book,* pages 12–13.❶

*What happened when you compared your predicted order to the order of the perimeters after you measured? Did anything surprise you about the perimeters of these shapes?*❷ ❸

Students might say:

 "I thought that the star would have the shortest perimeter, because it doesn't take up much space, but when I measured it, the perimeter was the longest."

 "I was surprised that the rectangle had a longer perimeter than the square."

 "The circle was the hardest one for me to predict."

Have students share the actual order of the perimeters of the shapes— circle (approximately seven inches), square (eight inches), rectangle (nine inches), and star (ten inches).

Many of you were surprised that the star has the longest perimeter. How is the star like the other shapes? How is it different? Why do you think it has the longest perimeter?

Teaching Note

❶ **When to Have this Discussion** If a number of students have not yet completed *Student Activity Book* pages 12–13, you might choose to begin this session with the Math Workshop and hold this discussion after the majority of students have completed the activity.

Math Notes

❷ **Area Versus Perimeter** Students may initially look at the area of each shape (the amount of space each one covers) when they make their predictions about the order of the perimeters of the shapes. Consequently, since the star is compact, they may inaccurately predict that it has the shortest perimeter and may fail to consider the number of sides the star has, and how those sides add to the overall perimeter.

❸ **Measuring Around a Circle** Perimeter is a *general* term that applies to the measure around the outside edge of all 2-D shapes. The term "circumference," on the other hand, is used *specifically* when referring to the perimeter of a circle. We have chosen to use the term perimeter in the context of this lesson, since we are comparing the measure of the length of the outside edge of a variety of shapes. Point out to students that the perimeter of a circle has a special name and use the term "circumference" from time to time when referring to the perimeter of the circle.

Students may comment that the star is about the same "size" as the square and circle, but that it has more sides and these sides add to the length of the perimeter.

Let's "stretch out" the perimeters of these shapes into straight lines so that we can have another way to compare them. That may help us see why the star has the longest perimeter. How long are the sides of the square? Can someone draw a line on the board combining those lengths? How about the rectangle? Can someone else draw that?

Continue until the perimeters of all four shapes are represented by straight lines on the board.

Did stretching out the perimeters into straight lines help you understand why the star has the longest perimeter? Can you explain what you think?

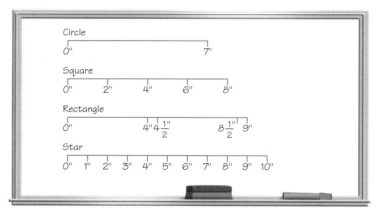

MATH WORKSHOP

2 Perimeter Problems

30 MIN

Students return to the Math Workshop activities of the previous two sessions. This half hour provides time for students to finish any unfinished work and for you to record observations of students who have not yet measured the perimeter of the large shape. Students who have finished these activities can be challenged with the extensions listed below or can work on the *LogoPaths* activity, *Missing Measures*. Check in briefly with students to make sure they understand what activities they should be working on.

2A Perimeter Problems

PAIRS

For details about this activity, see Session 1.3, page 40.

DIFFERENTIATION: Supporting the Range of Learners

Extension Students who finished the problems on *Student Activity Book* pages 9–10 can be challenged to find other shapes with perimeters of 100 feet or a shape for Pilar's yard with a perimeter of 200 feet. They can also be challenged to find shapes other than rectangles with perimeters of 20 centimeters.

2B Assessment: Measuring Perimeter

GROUPS

Observe any remaining students using Assessment Checklist: Measuring Perimeter (M14) to record your observations.

For details about this activity, see Session 1.3, page 41.

2C Ordering Shapes by Perimeter

PAIRS

For details about this activity, see Session 1.4, page 47.

2D *LogoPaths* Activity: *Missing Measures* (optional)

PAIRS **INDIVIDUALS**

For details about this activity, see Session 1.4, page 48.

ACTIVITY

15 MIN **CLASS**

3 Introducing *Quick Images: 2-D*

Quick Images: 2-D is introduced in this session and will continue as a Ten-Minute Math activity throughout Investigations 2 and 3. The *Quick Images* in this unit show various 2-D geometric figures. These arrangements are designed to give students practice in visualizing geometric images either as a whole or by decomposing them into memorable parts. As in all *Quick Images* activities, students see an image briefly, draw it, and then have the opportunity to refine their drawing as they view the image again. The students' task is to draw and then describe how they saw each figure. ❹

Teaching Note

❹ **Quick Images** For a complete description of this activity, see Part 4: Ten-Minute Math in *Implementing Investigations in Grade 3: Quick Images.*

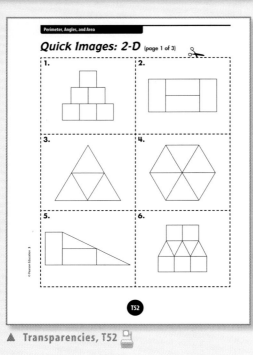

▲ **Transparencies, T52**

Differentiation

⑤ **English Language Learners** English Language Learners may need support to prepare them to explain how they visualized and drew the Quick Images. If possible, meet with them before this activity to introduce or review prepositions and prepositional phrases, such as *on top of, next to, over, under, in the middle,* and so on. Display structures built with connecting cubes or pattern blocks and ask students questions to help them describe what they see. *What color cube is in the middle of my building? What color cube is under the blue cube? Elena, can you put a yellow cube on top of the red one?* Students can take turns building structures for other students to draw and describe.

Display Image 1 from *Quick Images: 2-D* (T52).

Students briefly view a Quick Images *pattern and then sketch what they saw.*

Show students the image for three seconds before covering it or turning off the overhead projector. Students sketch what they saw. After one or two minutes have passed, show the image again for three seconds, and allow students to revise their drawings based on this second viewing. When student activity subsides again, show the image a third time. This time, leave it visible so that all students can complete or revise their drawings. ⑤

When students have finished, raise the following questions:

How were you able to remember this quick image after seeing it briefly?

What did you notice in the image that helped you? . . . How would you describe the figure you saw?

Students might say:

 "It reminded me of stacking blocks. Then I noticed that there were three on the bottom, then two, then one at the top."

 "I counted six squares altogether—one, then two, then three. That's six."

Repeat the same steps of this procedure using Image 2.

SESSION FOLLOW-UP
4 Daily Practice

Daily Practice: For reinforcement of this unit's content, have students complete *Student Activity Book* page 17.

Student Math Handbook: Students and families may use *Student Math Handbook* pages 110–111, 112–113 for reference and review. See pages 160–164 in the back of this unit.

Name _____ Date _____

Perimeter, Angles, and Area   Daily Practice

Building Shapes

Aaron combined two of these shapes to make a new shape.

NOTE Students combine shapes and find the perimeter of the new shape.
112–113

Here is the new shape Aaron made.

1. What is the perimeter of Aaron's new shape? _____

2. Combine the rectangle and the square. Draw the new shape. Find the perimeter. _____

3. Combine the square and the triangle. Draw the new shape. Find the perimeter. _____

Session 1.5   Unit 4   17

▲ **Student Activity Book, p. 17**

Mathematical Emphases

Features of Shape Describing and classifying 2-dimensional figures

Math Focus Points

◆ Determining the geometric moves needed (slides, flips, turns) to prove or disprove congruence between two shapes

Area Measurement Understanding and finding area

Math Focus Points

◆ Understanding that area is measured in square units

◆ Understanding that when measuring area, the space being measured must be completely covered with no gaps or overlaps

◆ Using squares and triangles to make shapes with an area of four square units

◆ Examining the relationship between the area of squares and triangles

◆ Understanding that shapes with the same area can look different

◆ Finding the area of partially covered rectangles

◆ Finding the area of an irregular shape

◆ Designing a shape for a given area

◆ Finding area by counting or calculating whole and partial square units

Linear Measurement Understanding and finding perimeter

Math Focus Points

◆ Finding the perimeter of an irregular shape

Understanding and Finding Area

	Student Activity Book	Student Math Handbook	Professional Development: Read Ahead of Time	
SESSION 2.1 p. 62				
Tetrominoes Students find all possible arrangements of four squares, called tetrominoes, and use transformations (flips, turns, slides) to prove whether or not one shape is the same as another. They use tetrominoes to cover the area of an 8 by 10 grid.	18–21	114, 116, 117	• **Teacher Note:** What's an -Omino?, p. 143	
SESSION 2.2 p. 68				
Which Tetrominoes Fit? Students discuss the meaning of area and find the area of an 8 by 10 rectangle. They continue covering the 8 by 10 rectangle with different tetromino shapes and discuss which shapes completely cover the rectangle.	18–20 22–23	114, 116		
SESSION 2.3 p. 74				
Squares and Triangles Students use squares (1 unit) and triangles ($\frac{1}{2}$ unit) to cover a tetromino puzzle. They focus on the square unit being the unit of measure for area, no matter what shape they are covering.	25–27	115	• **Teacher Note:** Understanding the Area of Triangles, p. 144 • **Dialogue Box:** The Space is the Same, p. 155	
SESSION 2.4 p. 81				
Area Activities Students begin a 3-day Math Workshop focusing on area. They create shapes with a given area, find the area of partially covered rectangles, and work on an optional *LogoPaths* activity in which they create rectangles with a perimeter of 200 steps.	28–32	114, 115		

Materials to Gather	Materials to Prepare
• **T55, 8 x 10 Rectangle** 📇 (optional) • **Connecting cubes** (100 per pair)	• **M16, 8 x 10 Rectangle** Make 2 copies per student. (optional) • **Tetrominoes** Make several samples using 4 interlocking cubes.
• **T55, 8 x 10 Rectangle** 📇 (optional) • **Connecting cubes** (120 per pair)	
• **Scissors** (1 per student) • **Glue** (as needed) • **Computers with** *LogoPaths* **software installed**	• **M17, Square and Triangle Cutouts** Make 1 copy per student for use in this session plus extras for use throughout this Investigation. • **T56, Square and Triangle Cutouts** Cut apart, 📇 (optional)
• **T56, Square and Triangle Cutouts** (from Session 2.3) • **Scissors** • **Glue** (as needed) • **12″ x 18″ construction paper** (1 per pair) • **Computers with** *LogoPaths* **software installed**	• **M17, Square and Triangle Cutouts** (1 per student; from Session 2.3) • **M4,** *LogoPaths: 200 Steps* Make copies. (1 per student)

📇 Overhead Transparency

Understanding and Finding Area, *continued*

SESSION 2.5	p. 88	Student Activity Book	Student Math Handbook	Professional Development: Read Ahead of Time
Area Activities, *continued* Students continue Math Workshop activities that focus on area and are introduced to a new Math Workshop activity—finding the perimeter and area of an irregular shape, their footprint.		28, 29–30, 33–34	112–113, 114, 115	

SESSION 2.6	p. 94			
Assessment: Make a Shape Students complete an assessment on creating a shape with an area of 5–7 square units. They continue Math Workshop activities focusing on area and discuss finding the perimeter and area of an irregular shape.		28, 29–30, 33, 35–36	112–113, 114, 115	• **Teacher Note:** Assessment: Make a Shape, p. 145 • **Dialogue Box:** Finding Perimeter and Area, p. 156

Materials to Gather	Materials to Prepare
• **M17, Square and Triangle Cutouts** (1 per student; from Session 2.3) • **Scissors** • **Glue** (as needed) • **12″ x 18″ construction paper** (1 per pair) • **Computers installed with *LogoPaths* software** • **Rulers** • **String/yarn** (as needed) • **Range of manipulatives** (color tiles, connecting cubes, etc.)	• **M5, *LogoPaths: 400 Steps*** Make 1 copy per student. • **M18, Three-Fourths-Inch Grid Paper** Make 1 copy per student. • **M19, Centimeter Grid Paper** Make 1 copy per student. • **Plain paper** Outline your footprint (in socks) on a sheet of plain paper.
• **Scissors** • **Glue** (as needed) • **12″ x 18″ construction paper** (1 per pair) • **Rulers** • **String/yarn** (as needed) • **Range of manipulatives** (color tiles, connecting cubes, etc.)	• **M20, Assessment: Make a Shape** Make 1 copy per student. • **M6, *LogoPaths: 500 Steps*** Make 1 copy per student. • **M18, Three-Fourths-Inch Grid Paper** Make 1 copy per student. • **M19, Centimeter Grid Paper** Make 1 copy per student.

Tetrominoes

Math Focus Points

◆ Determining the geometric moves needed (slides, flips, turns) to prove or disprove congruence between two shapes

◆ Understanding that area is measured in square units

◆ Understanding that when measuring area, the space being measured must be completely covered with no gaps or overlaps

Vocabulary

tetromino
flip
turn
slide
congruent

Today's Plan		Materials
ACTIVITY ❶ **Making Tetrominoes**	20 MIN INDIVIDUALS PAIRS	• Connecting cubes
DISCUSSION ❷ **Flips and Turns**	15 MIN CLASS	• Tetrominoes* (from Activity 1)
ACTIVITY ❸ **Covering a Rectangle**	25 MIN GROUPS PAIRS INDIVIDUALS	• *Student Activity Book,* p. 18; pp. 19–20 • M16*; T55 (optional) • Connecting cubes
SESSION FOLLOW-UP ❹ **Daily Practice**		• *Student Activity Book,* p. 21 • *Student Math Handbook,* pp. 114, 116, 117

*See *Materials to Prepare,* p. 59.

Ten-Minute Math

Quick Images: 2-D Show Images 3 and 4 (one at a time) from *Quick Images: 2-D* (T52) and follow the procedure for the basic routine. For each image, students discuss how they drew their figures, including any revisions they made after each viewing.

Ask students:

• How did you remember the parts of the image?

• What did you notice about the relationship of the parts of the image?

• What helped you remember the whole image, so you could draw your design?

ACTIVITY

① Making Tetrominoes

20 MIN INDIVIDUALS PAIRS

Challenge students to generate all possible arrangements of four cubes that are connected, lie flat, and are not stacked. If your students are familiar with dominoes, introduce the activity by asking students to share what they know about dominoes.❶ ❷

We form a domino by putting two squares together, and there's only one shape we can make. It doesn't matter how we turn or move the domino, there's only one shape. Today, you're going to be making shapes by putting four squares together, only you'll be using four connecting cubes. These shapes are called tetrominoes. Find out how many different shapes you can make. The cubes must be connected with full sides touching, and lie flat.

Students use connecting cubes to make as many different tetrominoes as possible.

After students have worked individually for ten minutes or so, call the group together.

Do you think you have all the shapes? How do you know? Work with a partner for the next ten minutes or so to see if you agree you have all the possible shapes. Then we'll discuss how you know. We're also going to name each of these shapes, so be thinking about what we should call them.❸

Teaching Note

❶ **Using Connecting Cubes** The two main focuses of this 2-D geometry session are: 1) for students to understand that shapes can be slid, turned, or flipped to show congruence and 2) using the tetromino shapes to cover the area of a 8 by 10 rectangle. Any material (color tiles or grid paper) used to make the tetrominoes are, of course, 3-D shapes. It is the top or bottom face that actually forms the tetromino. Using connecting cubes is recommended because the built tetrominoes are joined together so they are one piece and can be more easily slid, rotated, or flipped. Color tiles may be used to make the tetrominoes; however, since the color tiles cannot be joined it is much more difficult for students to use transformational geometry to prove congruence.

❸ **Focusing on Congruence** As students are working, continually ask them to prove how they know if the tetrominoes are the same or different. Point to two tetrominoes (sometimes to two that are different, and other times point to two that you notice are congruent) and ask students to prove if the tetrominoes are congruent or not.

Professional Development

❷ **Teacher Note:** What's an -Omino?, p. 143

ONGOING ASSESSMENT: Observing Students at Work

Students find all possible arrangements of four connected squares (tetrominoes).

- **Are students able to make all five tetrominoes?**

- **How do students decide if the shapes are the same or not?**
  Are they using slides, flips, and turns?

As students work with a partner, ask questions such as:

- Have you found all of the shapes? How do you know?

- When you compared shapes with a partner, how did you decide if the shapes were the same or different?

- How can you move your tetromino to see if it's the same shape? Can you flip it, or turn it, or slide it?

- What do you think we should call this shape?

DISCUSSION

2 Flips and Turns

15 MIN   CLASS

Math Focus Points for Discussion

◆ Determining the geometric moves needed (slides, flips, turns) to prove or disprove congruence between two shapes

There are only a certain number of tetromino shapes. Let's find out if we have them all. Who will come to the overhead and share one of their shapes?

Have students place a tetromino on the overhead. Ask how many students found the same shape. Ask if anyone thinks they have a different shape. Leave the shape on the overhead.

Who thinks they made a different shape?

The student should place the new shape on the overhead. Ask if the new tetromino is a different shape, and how students know. Accept responses, making sure students are describing the shape and convincing others. At this point, accept students' informal ideas and language as they discuss the motions they use on a tetromino to demonstrate that it is just like another; at the same time, you can use the terms slide, flip, and turn to describe their motions as the students show what they are doing on the overhead projector. If two tetrominoes are the same, remind students we call these congruent shapes.

Repeat this procedure until all five tetrominoes are on the overhead.

A student explains why a tetromino placed on the overhead is the same as the one across from it.

We're going to keep using these tetrominoes in future sessions, and it will be helpful if we all call them by the same name. What should we call each tetromino?

Help your class quickly agree on what each shape will be called throughout the rest of the investigation. Students often call these shapes by a letter name—T, L, Z, or by their shape—the square, the stairs, and so on.

ACTIVITY

③ Covering a Rectangle

25 MIN GROUPS PAIRS INDIVIDUALS

Although students work alone or with a partner on this activity, seat them in groups of four to six students for the initial preparation work. In each small group, have students use cubes to make sets of 10–15 of each of the five different tetrominoes (e.g., one student would make 10–15 of the "I" shape, another would make 10–15 of the "L" shape, and so on.) This way each individual or pair will have access to a set of each tetromino when the activity begins.

Teaching Note

❹ Limiting the Number of Tetrominoes Limiting students to only 10–15 tetrominoes encourages them to look for patterns, and to predict whether or not the given shape will completely cover the rectangle. If students are still unsure, they should build more tetrominoes. Students are likely to notice that if one of the tetrominoes completely fills one or two rows or columns on the rectangle, then that tetromino will completely cover the entire rectangle with no gaps or overlaps.

Math Note

❺ Unit of Measure and Understanding Area In this activity, which continues in Session 2.2, the tetromino is being used as the "unit of measure" for an area. The mathematical focus is on understanding area as completely covering the space and not in finding the area of the rectangle. The idea of squares and square units is introduced in Session 2.2, but the focus remains on understanding what area is, not on how to count it.

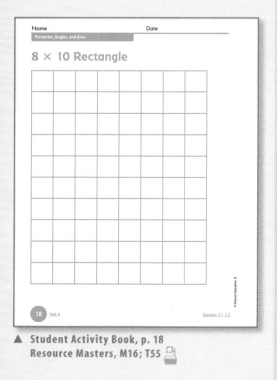

▲ **Student Activity Book, p. 18**
Resource Masters, M16; T55

Once most building activity has ceased, direct students' attention to *Student Activity Book* page 18, and *Student Activity Book* pages 19–20.

Today and tomorrow you'll work with the tetrominoes to cover the 8 by 10 rectangle. You may work alone or with a partner.

Go over the directions on *Student Activity Book* page 19 with students, and clarify any questions they might have. Students should try to determine whether or not the shape will cover the entire rectangle. Remind them that for a tetromino to be a "perfect cover-up" the shape has to completely cover the entire rectangle.

You can't have any cubes hanging over or sticking out the sides of the rectangle. Also remember to keep them flat—no cubes sticking up in a second layer.❹

Students use tetromino shapes to cover a rectangle.

If students finish using one tetromino shape, have them choose another to see if it will completely cover the 8 by 10 rectangle. Students continue to find shapes that cover the 8 by 10 rectangle in the next session.❺

ONGOING ASSESSMENT: Observing Students at Work

Students cover an 8 by 10 rectangle with tetrominoes.

- **How do students arrange tetrominoes to cover squares?** Are they planning ahead or placing tetrominoes randomly?

- **Do students find larger units they can use (making larger rectangles) to cover the space?** For example, do they place the "L" or "I" or "square" shapes together to make 2 by 4 rectangles?

As students are working, ask them to consider questions such as these:

- Do you think this shape will completely cover the rectangle? How do you know? Is there a pattern you can use to help you cover the rectangle?

SESSION FOLLOW-UP

④ Daily Practice

Daily Practice: For ongoing review, have students complete *Student Activity Book* page 21.

Student Math Handbook: Students and families may use *Student Math Handbook* pages 114, 116, 117 for reference and review. See pages 160–164 in the back of this unit.

Name _____ Date _____
Perimeter, Angles, and Area   Daily Practice

How Many More?

Solve the following problems and show your solutions on the number lines provided.

NOTE Students find the missing number to make an addition equation correct.

1. $116 + $ _____ $= 250$

2. $94 + $ _____ $= 260$

3. $143 + $ _____ $= 300$

4. $167 + $ _____ $= 325$

Session 2.1   Unit 4   **21**

▲ Student Activity Book, p. 21

Name _____ Date _____
Perimeter, Angles, and Area

The Perfect Cover-Up (page 1 of 2)

1. Choose one of the tetromino shapes. Draw the shape in the first column of the chart on the next page. Use 10–15 of that shape to cover as many squares as you can on the 8 × 10 rectangle on page 18.

2. Do you think this shape will completely cover the whole rectangle? How do you know? Answer this question in the second column of the chart.

3. If you are not sure whether it will cover the entire rectangle, you can do one of the following:
   a. Build more of the same tetromino shape and continue to cover the rectangle.
   b. On the rectangle, color the tetromino shapes you have already covered. Color all 4 squares in one tetromino shape the same color, but make each tetromino a different color. Then, try to cover the rest of the rectangle by moving the tetromino shapes or by coloring where additional tetrominoes will fit.

4. Answer the questions in the other columns of the chart.

5. Repeat these steps with the other tetromino shapes.

Sessions 2.1, 2.2   Unit 4   **19**

▲ Student Activity Book, p. 19

Name _____ Date _____
Perimeter, Angles, and Area

The Perfect Cover-Up (page 2 of 2)

Tetromino Shape	Will it be a "perfect cover-up"? Yes or No	Why or why not?	How many cover the rectangle?

6. Which tetromino shapes were not a "perfect cover-up"? Explain why you think each one did not cover the 8 by 10 rectangle.

20   Unit 4   Sessions 2.1, 2.2

▲ Student Activity Book, p. 20

Which Tetrominoes Fit?

Math Focus Points

- Understanding that when measuring area, the space being measured must be completely covered with no gaps or overlaps
- Understanding that area is measured in square units

Vocabulary

area

Today's Plan		Materials
DISCUSSION **① What Is Area?**	10 MIN CLASS GROUPS	• *Student Activity Book,* p. 18 (from Session 2.1)
ACTIVITY **② The Perfect Cover-Up**	35 MIN GROUPS PAIRS INDIVIDUALS	• *Student Activity Book,* pp. 18–20 (from Session 2.1) • Connecting cubes
DISCUSSION **③ Which Tetrominoes Fit?**	15 MIN CLASS	• *Student Activity Book,* p. 20 (from Session 2.1) • T55 (optional)
SESSION FOLLOW-UP **④ Daily Practice and Homework**		• *Student Activity Book,* pp. 22–23 • *Student Math Handbook,* pp. 114, 116

*See *Materials to Prepare,* p. 59.

Ten-Minute Math

Quick Images: 2-D Show Images 5 and 6 (one at a time) from *Quick Images: 2-D* (T52) and follow the procedure for the basic routine. For each image, students discuss how they drew their figures, including any revisions they made after each viewing.

Ask students:

- How did you remember the parts of the image?
- What did you notice about the relationship of the parts of the image?
- What helped you remember the whole image, so you could draw your design?

DISCUSSION

① What Is Area?

10 MIN   CLASS   GROUPS

Math Focus Points for Discussion

◈ Understanding that when measuring area, the space being measured must be completely covered with no gaps or overlaps

Direct students' attention to *Student Activity Book* page 18.

You've been working with this 8 by 10 rectangle. What are some things about this rectangle you could measure?

Students will likely mention length, width, and perimeter. Some students may point out that the inside space (the area) can also be measured.

Remember all the measuring you did in Investigation 1? What tools did you use to measure?

Listen to students' responses about how they measured something linear. They are likely to mention rulers, yardsticks, and metersticks.

When you used these measurement tools in the past, you were finding out how high or wide or long an object was. In Investigation 1, you used these tools to find the perimeters of different shapes. There are also other kinds of things you need to measure. For example, you might want to figure out how big a rug must be to cover the floor in your room, or how much wallpaper you need to cover the walls in the kitchen. In those cases, you want to measure a certain amount of flat space. We call this measurement area.

Have students look at the blank 8 by 10 rectangle again.

When we measure length, we use units like inches or meters. When we measure area, like the surface of this tabletop, we use a square unit. How many squares are in this 8 by 10 rectangle? How do you know? Talk in your small groups about this.

Give students a few minutes to discuss this, and then collect answers.

Teaching Note

❶ Focus on Area as a 2-D Measure While students are using 3-D shapes for the tetrominoes, it is important to focus their attention on the top or bottom surface of these 3-D tetrominoes. Thus, they are concentrating on the amount of space they are covering on the rectangle. Ask students questions about how much space is being covered and about the unit of measure for area—a square unit.

If students are counting individual squares, encourage them to try counting by a larger number. Most students count by 10s and determine the rectangle has 80 square units. Some students will know that 10×8 is 80.

Students measure area by determining how many squares are in a rectangle.

So we would say this 8 by 10 rectangle has an area of 80 square units. When we find area, we have to cover all the space; we can't leave any spaces or gaps.❶

ACTIVITY

②The Perfect Cover-Up

35 MIN   GROUPS   PAIRS   INDIVIDUALS

Students continue to work individually or in pairs on *Student Activity Book* pages 19–20, but should remain seated with their small group to have access to all five tetrominoes. Individual students are not expected to use all five tetrominoes to cover the rectangle. However, each small group should work together to make sure that every tetromino has been tested. Inform students that at the end of the session, they will discuss which tetrominoes completely cover the 8 by 10 rectangle and talk about their answers on *Student Activity Book* pages 19–20.

Students work together to make sure every tetromino has been tested.

You're going to continue covering the 8 by 10 rectangle with tetrominoes. You can determine whether or not your shapes will work without covering the whole rectangle. Remember, you can turn or flip the shapes. As you work, be thinking about why some shapes are easier to use than others.

Students use a variety of strategies to decide if the tetromino completely covers the rectangle, including:

- Guess and check: A beginning strategy is simply to place tetrominoes where they look like they fit, and then to change the placement if large holes appear. As they continue with other tetrominoes, many students move beyond this and start thinking ahead, planning where each tetromino should go.

- Patterns: Some students see that putting one tetromino "this way," then the next one "that way," in a pattern, leads to a perfect cover-up (e.g., starting with the "L" shape and using a combination of flips, turns, and slides to form a 2 by 4 array).

ONGOING ASSESSMENT: Observing Students at Work

Students cover an 8 by 10 rectangle with tetrominoes.

- **After placing the first 10–15 tetrominoes on the rectangle, are students able to determine whether or not the entire rectangle will be completely covered?** What reasoning do they use? Or do they have to place all 30 tetrominoes on the rectangle?

- **How do students arrange tetrominoes to cover squares?** Are they planning ahead or placing tetrominoes randomly?

- **Do students find larger units they can use (making larger rectangles) to cover the space?** For example, do they place the "L" or "I" or "square" shapes together to make 2 by 4 rectangles?

As you observe students, ask questions such as:

- Can you make a "perfect fit" with the tetromino you chose? In other words, will it completely cover the 8 by 10 rectangle? Are there different ways to get a perfect fit with this tetromino? (Using slides, flips, and turns.)

- Are there any strategies you can use to get more of your tetromino to fit on the grid? (Using slides, flips, and turns.)

- I see you've put down 10 tetrominoes on the grid. Do you think your shape will completely cover the rectangle? How do you know? How many tetrominoes will it take?

- How many square units have you covered so far? How many more need to be covered?

- I see you're using a pattern. Will that lead to a perfect fit if it continues?

- You think this shape won't cover the rectangle completely. Why not?

DIFFERENTIATION: Supporting the Range of Learners

Extension Students who easily understand which single tetromino shapes completely cover the 8 by 10 rectangle can be challenged to use more than one type of tetromino (such as the L and the T) to completely cover the rectangle.

DISCUSSION
Which Tetrominoes Fit?

15 MIN   CLASS

Math Focus Points for Discussion

◆ Understanding that when measuring area, the space being measured must be completely covered with no gaps or overlaps

Use students responses to *Student Activity Book* pages 19–20 for this discussion. The transparency of the 8 by 10 rectangle (T55) on the overhead projector is useful for demonstrating students' strategies.

Which shapes worked to completely cover the rectangle? Does everyone agree? Anyone disagree? Why? Which shapes didn't work? Does everyone agree? Anyone disagree? Why? Why didn't these two shapes work?

Collect students' answers and have the class agree on which shapes did and did not work. Make certain students explain why these shapes do not work.

Students might say:

"The Z doesn't work. No matter what, a piece will hang over the edge of the rectangle. To make it work you'd have to cut some squares off or put it so it's covering part of another tetromino."

"The T doesn't work. It's the same problem as with the Z. Some of it will hang off the edge. It won't completely cover the rectangle unless you do something else like cut it, or leave empty spaces."

SESSION FOLLOW-UP
Daily Practice and Homework

Daily Practice: For ongoing review, have students complete *Student Activity Book* page 22.

Homework: Students look at a puzzle with missing pieces and choose pieces that will complete the puzzle on *Student Activity Book* page 23.

Student Math Handbook: Students and families may use *Student Math Handbook* pages 114, 116 for reference and review. See pages 160–164 in the back of this unit.

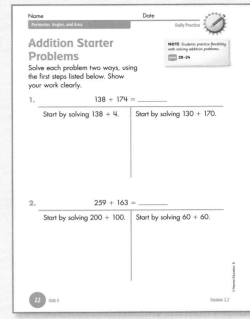

▲ Student Activity Book, p. 22

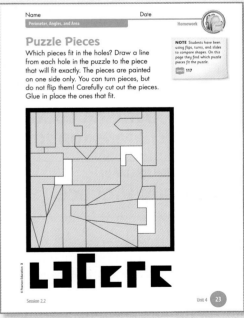

▲ Student Activity Book, p. 23

Squares and Triangles

Math Focus Points

◆ Using squares and triangles to make shapes with an area of four square units

◆ Examining the relationship between the area of squares and triangles

Today's Plan		Materials
ACTIVITY ① Introducing Tetromino Puzzle	🕐 👥 10 MIN CLASS	• *Student Activity Book,* pp. 25–26 • M17*
ACTIVITY ② Tetromino Puzzle	🕐 👤 35 MIN INDIVIDUALS	• *Student Activity Book,* pp. 25–26 • M17*; T56* (optional) • Scissors • Glue
DISCUSSION ③ Area of Triangles	🕐 👥 👥 15 MIN CLASS PAIRS	• *Student Activity Book,* pp. 25–26
ACTIVITY ④ Introducing *LogoPaths: 200 Steps* (optional)	👥 👥 CLASS GROUPS	• Computers with *LogoPaths* software installed
SESSION FOLLOW-UP ⑤ Daily Practice		• *Student Activity Book,* p. 27 • *Student Math Handbook,* p. 115

*See *Materials to Prepare,* p. 59.

Ten-Minute Math

Quick Images: 2-D Show Images 7 and 8 (one at a time) from *Quick Images: 2-D* (T53) and follow the procedure for the basic routine. For each image, students discuss how they drew their figures, including any revisions they made after each viewing.

Ask students:

• How did you remember the parts of the image?

• What did you notice about the relationship of the parts of the image?

• What helped you remember the whole image, so you could draw your design?

ACTIVITY

① Introducing Tetromino Puzzle

10 MIN   CLASS

We're going to continue thinking about area and about square units. ❶

If your classroom floor or ceiling is covered with square tiles, use these tiles as an example.

Look at our classroom floor. We could use the square tiles on the floor to measure the area of the floor. Or we can use the square tiles on the ceiling. Sometimes people use big squares to measure the area of space, like the square tiles on the floor. Sometimes they choose smaller squares for measuring area. Whatever the size of the square, it can be called a square unit.

Direct the students' attention to *Student Activity Book* pages 25–26.

For this puzzle, we are going to say that one of the squares on the page is one unit of area. Look at this paper. Talk to a neighbor about what you notice.

Give students a minute or two to do this, and then collect responses. Students should notice that these are the same tetromino shapes they have been using, only larger. If no student brings it up, ask,

What is the area of each of these tetrominoes?

Most students readily agree that each tetromino has an area of four square units.

Now look at a copy of Square and Triangle Cutouts (M17). What do you notice about the shapes on this sheet?

Give students a minute or two to do this; then collect responses. Students should notice that the shapes are squares and triangles, and that some triangles are larger than the others.

Math Note

❶ **Unit of Measure for Area** In Sessions 2.1 and 2.2, tetrominos were used as the unit of measure for the 8 × 10 rectangle. In this session, the tetromino becomes the shape being measured, and the square unit becomes the unit of measure.

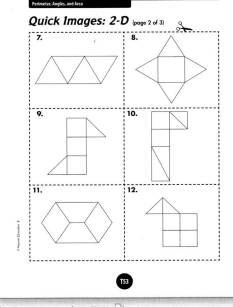

▲ Transparencies, T53

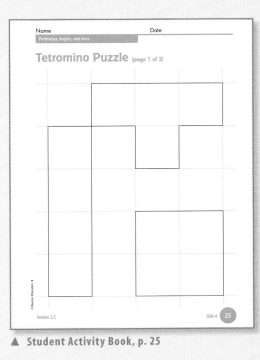

▲ Student Activity Book, p. 25

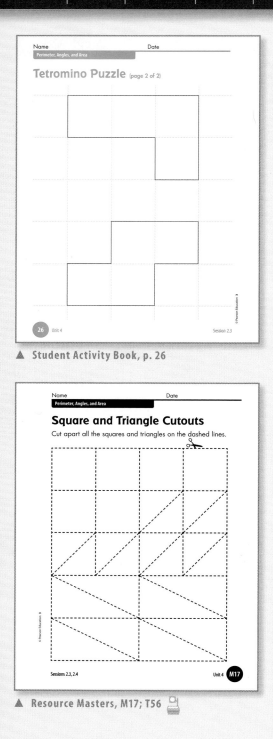

▲ Student Activity Book, p. 26

▲ Resource Masters, M17; T56

ACTIVITY
2 Tetromino Puzzle

Your task today is to cut out the squares and triangles and arrange them so they cover the five tetrominoes completely on the puzzle sheet. You may need to arrange and rearrange them to find a way to make the pieces fit. Remember, when you find area, everything has to be covered, and there can't be any gaps or overlaps. When you've found a way that they all fit, glue your pieces onto the tetrominoes on *Student Activity Book* pages 25–26.

Students arrange and rearrange shapes to completely cover the tetrominos on the puzzle sheet.

As students are working, use the vocabulary of flips, turns, and slides as they move their pieces around. Also ask about the area of the individual tetrominoes.

Find examples where triangles have been used to cover a tetromino. As you find them, draw them on the board or on an overhead to use for the discussion. Choose shapes that have at least two triangles and one square.

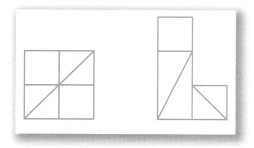

ONGOING ASSESSMENT: Observing Students at Work

Students use squares and triangles to cover tetrominoes.

- **Are students able to use the squares and triangles to cover the tetrominoes?**

- **Do students understand they have to completely cover the tetrominoes, leaving no gaps or overlaps?**

DIFFERENTIATION: Supporting the Range of Learners

Extension Students who easily complete the puzzles should be challenged to do the activity again, only this time assembling puzzle pieces to make the tetrominoes without using the outlines. Another challenge would be to use at least one triangle in each of the shapes.

DISCUSSION
Area of Triangles

15 MIN CLASS PAIRS

Math Focus Points for Discussion

◆ Examining the relationship between the area of squares and triangles

Point to one of the tetrominoes you have displayed on the board or overhead.❷

What is the area of this shape?

Students should remember that the area of each tetromino is four square units.

*So if the area of each tetromino is four square units, what is the area of each of the squares and triangles we have used? The squares are easy enough—they're each one square unit. But what about the triangles?*❸

Point to one of the smaller triangles.

What is the area of this triangle? How do you know? Discuss it with a partner.

Give students a minute to discuss this with a partner.

Professional Development

❷ **Teacher Note:** Understanding the Area of Triangles, p. 144
Dialogue Box: The Space is the Same, p. 155

Teaching Note

❸ **Finding the Area of Triangles** As students begin finding the area of triangles, it is important for them to understand that if a rectangle (including a square) is cut diagonally in half to form two triangles, each of these triangles is $\frac{1}{2}$ the area of the rectangle. In this activity, the small triangle is made by cutting a square in half diagonally, so each triangle has an area of $\frac{1}{2}$ square unit. The larger triangle is made by cutting a 1 by 2 rectangle in half diagonally, so each triangle has an area of one square unit.

Students might say:

 "Well, two of the small triangles make 1 square. So I think one small triangle is $\frac{1}{2}$ square unit."

 "When I cut out the small triangles, I put two together, and they covered the square, so each one has to be $\frac{1}{2}$ of the square."

Point to one of the larger triangles.

What is the area of this triangle? How do you know? Discuss it with a partner.

Students might say:

 "I think it's one. If you count the square and the smaller triangles, that's two square units. Since the tetromino has an area of four square units, the large triangle has to be one."

 "I think it's one, too. If you cut off the top of the triangle, and then taped the two pieces, you could make one square unit."

 "I made a shape and used two of the large triangles. It made a rectangle that was two square units. Since one triangle is $\frac{1}{2}$ the rectangle, it would have an area of one square unit."

A student demonstrates how he found the area of the larger triangle.

Most students are comfortable with the area of the smaller triangle being $\frac{1}{2}$ square unit, but may be uncertain about the area of the larger triangle. Students continue working with these shapes in the Math Workshop in the next session.

ACTIVITY

CLASS   GROUPS

Introducing *LogoPaths: 200 Steps* (optional)

In this activity, students use *Free Explore* in the *LogoPaths* software to draw rectangles with perimeters of 200 turtle steps. As with *Missing Measures*, students may enter commands of any amount, not just multiples of 10. While the software allows them to enter commands to make turning angles of any size, they will need to make right and left turns of 90 degrees in order to create rectangles.

Today you're going to learn a new activity called *200 Steps*. Your goal in this activity is to create as many rectangles as you can with perimeters of 200 turtle steps using the *LogoPaths* software. So, you'll have to use what you know about rectangles to think about what the lengths of the sides could be and what size turns the turtle needs to make. You can use any number for the length of the sides, not only multiples of 10. For example, if you want one side to be 65 steps, you enter **FD 65**.

Open *Free Explore* in the *LogoPaths* software. Have students suggest commands to draw the sides and make the angles needed to create a rectangle with a perimeter of 200 steps. Ask questions to help them explain and look for strategies in the numbers they choose.

[Bridget] said to use **FD 80** for the length of the first side? What does that tell you about how long the other sides will have to be to create a perimeter of 200 steps?

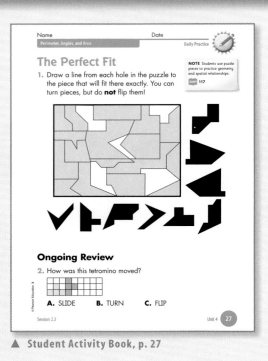

▲ **Student Activity Book, p. 27**

Students might say:

"Well, 80 will be the long side, so I know the short side has to be 20 because 80 plus 20 is 100. Another 80 plus 20 will make the perimeter 200."

"I was thinking that there has to be another side that's 80 because the opposite sides of rectangles are the same. So that would make 160 steps so far. That means that the other two sides would have to equal 40 steps together, or 20 steps each."

So we went forward 80 steps, but now we need to turn. What kind of turn do we need to make to create the kind of corner we need for a rectangle? Does anyone know what command we should use?

Students identified and used the term right angle in Grade 2, but did not identify these angles as 90 degrees. However, if they have played the game *Get the Toys*, they will be familiar with the commands **RT 90** and **LT 90** to turn the turtle right or left 90 degrees. If no one makes this connection, bring it up yourself and demonstrate how the right or left 90 commands will turn the turtle to form a right angle. Do not spend too much time on this. Students will see firsthand the effect of entering other angle sizes as they attempt to construct their rectangles in the 200 Steps activity.

Solicit further suggestions from the students. At the end of the procedure, use the **HT** (hide turtle) command to check whether or not the rectangle is complete. Then use the Label Lengths tool to label the length of each line segment and let students know they will do the same when they make their own rectangles. Students should also use the Teach tool to name and save the procedure for each rectangle they create.

SESSION FOLLOW-UP

⑤ Daily Practice

 Daily Practice: For reinforcement of this unit's content, have students complete *Student Activity Book* page 27.

 Student Math Handbook: Students and families may use *Student Math Handbook* page 115 for reference and review. See pages 160–164 in the back of this unit.

Area Activities

Math Focus Points

◆ Using squares and triangles to make shapes with an area of four square units

◆ Understanding that shapes with the same area can look different

◆ Finding the area of partially covered rectangles

Today's Plan		Materials
ACTIVITY **1 Introducing Shape Poster**	🕐 10 MIN 👥 CLASS	• T56 (from Session 2.3)
MATH WORKSHOP **2 Finding Area** **2A** Shape Poster **2B** What's the Area? **2C** *LogoPaths* Activity: *200 Steps* (optional)	🕐 35 MIN	**2A** • Student Activity Book, p. 28 • M17 • Scissors; glue; 12″ x 18″ construction paper **2B** • *Student Activity Book, pp. 29–30* **2C** • M4* • Computers with *LogoPaths* software installed
DISCUSSION **3 The Area's the Same**	🕐 15 MIN 👥 CLASS 👥 GROUPS	
SESSION FOLLOW-UP **4 Daily Practice and Homework**		• *Student Activity Book, pp. 31–32* • *Student Math Handbook, pp. 114, 115*

*See *Materials to Prepare*, p. 59.

Ten-Minute Math

Practicing Place Value Write 436 on the board and have students practice saying it to a partner. Make sure all students can read, write, and say this number correctly.

Ask students:

• Find and sketch 5–6 different ways to make 436 using only sheets of 100, strips of 10 and single stickers (such as, 3 sheets, 10 strips and 36 singles or 2 sheets, 10 strips and 136 singles).

Collect a few examples on the board and ask students how they found their answers.

Did anyone notice a pattern?

ACTIVITY

1 Introducing *Shape Poster*

10 MIN · CLASS

Let students know that the next three sessions are a Math Workshop, focusing on finding and understanding area. Students also have the option of working on the *LogoPaths* activity, *200 Steps*, in which they create different rectangles with a perimeter of 200 steps.

We're about to start a 3-day Math Workshop. Today there are three activities. In one, you find the area of rectangles when part of the rectangle can't be seen. Another is working on a new *LogoPaths* computer activity. And the third is making a *Shape Poster*, using the triangles and squares you used in the last session.

To make your shape posters, you'll use the square and triangle cutouts, and you'll make different shapes that have an area of four square units. There are two rules to follow as you make new shapes.

Use either cut out squares and triangles on the overhead from Square and Triangle Cutouts (T56) or draw figures on the board to illustrate the two rules.

Rule 1: Each new shape, like tetrominoes, must have "full sides touching." For example, these three shapes are OK:

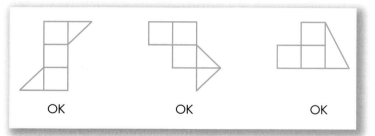

These shapes are *not* OK, because full sides do not always match, or only corners are touching:

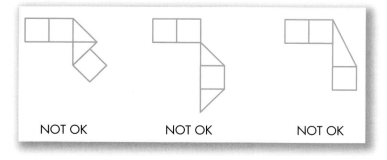

Rule 2: Each shape should be different from any others on the poster. In this case, "different" means that shapes are not congruent through rotation or reflection (turns and flips). For example, these two shapes are the same—one is a rotation of the other.

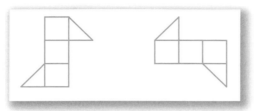

If you can lay one whole shape on top of another whole shape, it is considered the same shape. These two shapes are the same because their outline is the same, even though they are made with different pieces.

MATH WORKSHOP

2 Finding Area

35 MIN

Go over the directions for the remaining activities with students, making certain they understand the tasks. Also tell students that the discussion at the end of the session today focuses on their shape posters, so each pair needs to have at least three shapes on its poster.

2A Shape Poster

PAIRS

Using *Student Activity Book* page 28, students work with a partner to cut out squares and triangles and to make different shapes that have an area of four square units.

As pairs work on their shape posters, it is likely they will have congruent shapes. Ask students to use slides, flips, and turns to prove whether or not shapes are congruent.

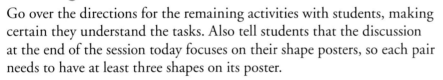

▲ **Student Activity Book, p. 28**

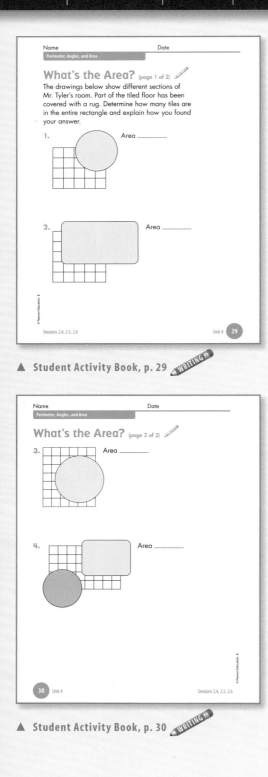

▲ Student Activity Book, p. 29

▲ Student Activity Book, p. 30

ONGOING ASSESSMENT: Observing Students at Work

Students make shapes with four square units.

- **Do students understand that the large triangle has an area of one square unit, and the small triangle has an area of $\frac{1}{2}$ square unit?**

- **Are students able to explain how they know their shape has an area of four square units?** ("I used two squares and two large triangles. Each large triangle is the same as one square, so that's four square units.")

2B What's the Area?
PAIRS INDIVIDUALS

In the *Student Activity Book,* on pages 29–30, students find the area of large rectangles that have one or more corners covered in some way. The fourth rectangle is the most difficult as it has two corners covered.

Students may either work alone or with a partner on this activity.

ONGOING ASSESSMENT: Observing Students at Work

Students determine the area of rectangles that are partially covered.

- **How do students compute the total area?** Do they draw the shape again on grid paper and count each unit? Do they draw the units over the top of the diagram? Do they count by individual units or use rows or columns?

DIFFERENTIATION: Supporting the Range of Learners

(**Intervention**) Students having difficulty picturing the entire rectangle will benefit from drawing the complete rectangle on a piece of grid paper (without the "rugs") so they can see each square unit.

2C *LogoPaths* Activity: *200 Steps*
PAIRS INDIVIDUALS

Students work alone or with partners on this *LogoPaths* activity in which they use *LogoPaths* commands to build different rectangles with perimeters of 200 steps. They build as many rectangles as they can with this perimeter. They record the commands they used and choose four of the rectangles to sketch and label on *LogoPaths: 200 Steps* (M4).

ONGOING ASSESSMENT: Observing Students at Work

Students use their understanding of perimeter and the structure of rectangles to create different rectangles with perimeters of 200 steps.

- **Can students use *LogoPaths* commands fluently?**

- **Do they accurately use right and left turns even when the turtle is not facing straight up?**

- **Do students demonstrate understanding that in order to make rectangles they must use turns of 90 degrees?**

- **Do students demonstrate knowledge that parallel sides of rectangles must be equal?**

- **Are they able to create multiple rectangles with perimeters of 200 steps?** Is this by trial and error or do they have a strategy to find new rectangles with the same perimeter (e.g., recognizing that if they have a rectangle with side lengths of 70, 30, 70, 30, they can subtract the same number of steps from one pair of parallel sides and add them to the other pair of parallel sides to create a 200 perimeter rectangle with side lengths of 65, 35, 65, 35)?

- **Is one of the rectangles they create a square?**

- **Can they create rectangles with perimeters of 200 that have sides with lengths that are not multiples of 10?**

DIFFERENTIATION: Supporting the Range of Learners

Extension Students who appear to be moving easily through this activity are probably using a strategy to help them create new rectangles. Help them think about whether or not their strategy would work with any rectangle. Ask questions like the following:

- I see you made a rectangle with sides 70, 30, 70, and 30 steps long. Can you start with that rectangle and make another one that would also have a perimeter of 200 steps?

- Could you use that strategy again to turn your new rectangle into another one that works? Do you think your strategy would work with any rectangle?

Name _____ **Date** _____

Perimeter, Angles, and Area

LogoPaths: 200 Steps

Use *LogoPaths Free Explore* to make rectangles with perimeters of 200 turtle steps. Make sure that some of your rectangles have sides that are not multiples of 10. If you can, make a square with a perimeter of 200 steps. Use the **Teach** tool to name your solutions. Save your work when you have finished.

Sketch at least four of the rectangles you made in the space below. Label the length of each side.

M4   Unit 4

▲ Resource Masters, M4

DISCUSSION

③ The Area's the Same

15 MIN CLASS GROUPS

Math Focus Points for Discussion

◆ Understanding that shapes with the same area can look different

Before the discussion begins, have three to four students draw one of the shapes they made for their shape poster on the board or overhead.

Students show shapes they created for their shape posters.

Are these shapes all different from each other? How do you know?

Students should use flips, turns, and slides to prove the shapes are different (or the same.)

The task was to create shapes that had an area of four square units. How do we know if each of these shapes has four square units?

Have students explain how they know if the shape has an area of four square units. Student explanations should include counting the smaller triangle as $\frac{1}{2}$ square unit, and the larger triangle as one square unit.

Ask students if there are ways they could write numbers on the shapes to show that they contain four square units.

How could we count the squares and triangles to show these shapes have an area of four square units?

Students generally use two kinds of labeling to prove that shapes are four square units.

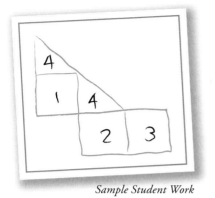

Sample Student Work

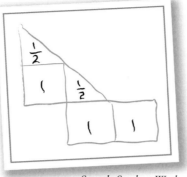

Sample Student Work

In Session 2.5, students are asked to find perimeter and area. To review perimeter, ask students to consider the shapes on the board or overhead.

Even though these shapes all look different, they all have an area of four square units. Do they all have the same perimeter? How do we know?

Give students a minute or so to discuss this in small groups, and then ask students to explain what they are thinking. It is not important to find the exact perimeter of these shapes. Students should recognize however, that the shapes do not all have the same perimeter.

SESSION FOLLOW-UP
4 Daily Practice and Homework

 Daily Practice: For ongoing review, have students complete *Student Activity Book* page 31.

 Homework: Students practice solving missing addend problems on *Student Activity Book* page 32.

Student Math Handbook: Students and families may use *Student Math Handbook* pages 114, 115 for reference and review. See pages 160–164 in the back of this unit.

Name _____ Date _____
Perimeter, Angles, and Area — Daily Practice

Class Collections

For each problem, write an equation, solve the problem, and show your solution. You may use a number line or your 1,000 chart to help you solve these problems.

NOTE Students find the difference between 3-digit numbers. Ask your child to explain how he or she solves each problem. *Unit* 29–30, 32–35, 106

1. The students in Ms. Ahmed's class are collecting bottle caps. Their goal is to collect 500. They have 317 so far. How many more do they need to reach their goal?

2. The students in Ms. Kennedy's class are collecting pennies. Their goal is to collect $7.00. So far they have 426 pennies. How many more do they need to reach their goal?

Ongoing Review

3. The perimeter of a rectangle is 39 centimeters. The perimeter of a circle is 39 inches. Which statement about the two shapes is correct?

   A. The rectangle has a larger perimeter.
   B. The circle has a larger perimeter.
   C. The rectangle and the circle have the same perimeter.

Session 2.4 — Unit 4 **31**

▲ **Student Activity Book, p. 31**

Name _____ Date _____
Perimeter, Angles, and Area — Homework

Make Some Frog Jumps

Answer the questions below, and explain how you solved the problem.

NOTE Students practice solving addition problems by finding 3 or 4 addends that equal the given sum.

1. Three frogs jumped a total of 115 centimeters. How far could each frog have jumped?

   Frog 1 _____ Frog 2 _____ Frog 3 _____

   How did you solve it?

2. Four frogs jumped a total of 185 centimeters. How far could each frog have jumped?

   Frog 1 _____ Frog 2 _____ Frog 3 _____ Frog 4 _____

   How did you solve it?

32 Unit 4 — Session 2.4

▲ **Student Activity Book, p. 32**

Area Activities, *continued*

Math Focus Points

◆ Finding the area of partially covered rectangles

◆ Finding the area of an irregular shape

◆ Finding the perimeter of an irregular shape

Today's Plan		Materials
ACTIVITY **① Introducing How Big Is Your Foot?**	15 MIN CLASS	• Drawing of your footprint*
MATH WORKSHOP **② Finding Area** **2A** *Shape Poster* **2B** What's the Area? **2C** *LogoPaths* Activity: *400 Steps* (optional) **2D** How Big Is Your Foot?	35 MIN	**2A** • Materials from Session 2.4, p. 81 **2B** • Materials from Session 2.4, p. 81 **2C** • M5* • Computers with *LogoPaths* software installed **2D** • *Student Activity Book*, p. 33 • M18*; M19* • Rulers; string/yarn; range of manipulatives (color tiles, connecting cubes, etc.)
DISCUSSION **③ What's the Area?**	10 MIN CLASS PAIRS	• *Student Activity Book*, pp. 29–30 (from Session 2.4)
SESSION FOLLOW-UP **④ Daily Practice**		• *Student Activity Book*, p. 34 • *Student Math Handbook*, pp. 112–113, 114, 115

*See *Materials to Prepare*, p. 61.

Ten-Minute Math

Practicing Place Value Say "two hundred sixty-three" and ask students to write the number. Make sure all students can read, write, and say this number correctly. Ask students to solve these problems mentally, if possible:

• What is 263 + 30? 263 − 20? 263 − 50? 263 + 300? 263 − 200? 263 + 500?

Write each number on the board. Ask students to compare each sum or difference with 263.

Which places have the same digits? Which do not? Why?

If time remains, pose additional similar problems.

ACTIVITY

Introducing How Big Is Your Foot?

15 MIN   CLASS

Display the drawing of your footprint that you prepared ahead of time.❶

Earlier this year, you measured the length of your feet. Look at this footprint. I made it by taking off my shoe and tracing the outline of my foot on this paper. You could use the outline to measure how long my foot is. What are some other things about my foot that you could measure?

Accept student responses. Students should suggest that they could measure the perimeter and the area.

In our Math Workshop today and tomorrow, your task is to find out the perimeter and the area of your foot. You'll start by tracing the outline of one foot onto a piece of paper. Remember to take your shoes off but keep your socks on.

Have students look at the directions for this activity on *Student Activity Book* page 33. Clarify any questions they might have.

At the end of the session today, we'll be discussing Problem 1 from Student Activity Book page 29, so be sure you complete that problem today.

MATH WORKSHOP

Finding Area

35 MIN

Students continue working on activities focusing on area. It is expected most students will need this session to work exclusively on the How Big is Your Foot? and What's the Area? activities. Students will have additional time in Session 2.6 to finish their Shape Posters, if they have not already done so. Check in with students to make sure they are clear on which activities they will work on during today's session.

Students who have time can work on the *LogoPaths* activity, *400 Steps*. If they did not work on *200 Steps* in the previous Math Workshop, they should complete that activity before moving on to *400 Steps*.

Name _____ Date _____

Perimeter, Angles, and Area

How Big Is Your Foot? ✏

Find the perimeter and area of your foot.
Then answer the following questions.

1. What is the perimeter of your foot?

   Describe how you measured the perimeter.

2. What is the area of your foot?

   Explain how you found your answer.

Sessions 2.5, 2.6   Unit 4   33

▲ **Student Activity Book, p. 33**

▲ Resource Masters, M5

Name _____ Date _____

Perimeter, Angles, and Area

LogoPaths: 400 Steps

Use *LogoPaths Free Explore* to make rectangles with perimeters of 400 turtle steps. Make sure that some of your rectangles have sides that are not multiples of 10. If you can, make a square with a perimeter of 400 steps. Use the **Teach** tool to name your solutions. Save your work when you have finished.

Sketch at least four of the rectangles you made in the space below. Label the length of each side.

Unit 4 M5

2A Shape Poster

PAIRS

See Session 2.4 (page 83) for a complete description of this activity.

2B What's the Area?

PAIRS INDIVIDUALS

Students need to complete at least Problem 1 on *Student Activity Book* page 29 for the discussion at the end of this session.

See Session 2.4, page 84 for a complete description of this activity.

2C LogoPaths Activity: *400 Steps* (optional)

PAIRS INDIVIDUALS

Students who completed the *200 Steps* activity in the previous Math Workshop can move on to *400 Steps,* following the same procedure as the *200 Steps* activity. Using the *LogoPaths* software, they build as many rectangles as they can with the perimeter of 400 steps. They record the commands they used and choose four rectangles to sketch and label on *LogoPaths: 400 Steps* (M5).

See Session 2.4, page 84.

2D How Big Is Your Foot?

PAIRS INDIVIDUALS

Students trace an outline of their feet and find its perimeter and area.

Students work individually or in pairs to find the perimeter and area of their feet.

Students find two challenges in this work. One is how to determine the perimeter of their feet. If students are using rulers, ask them how they know their measurement is accurate, or what is difficult about measuring a curved line with a straight edge. Remind students of the work they did measuring perimeter in Investigation 1 and ask how they measured the perimeter of shapes with curved edges (using string or adding machine tape). Once one or two students realize they can use string, or something similar, to outline their foot and can then measure the string, most students will use that strategy.

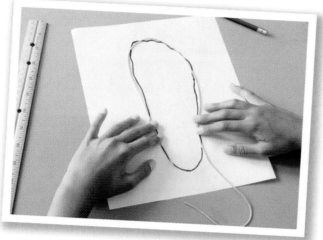

Students realize that string works well to measure the perimeter of their feet.

Finding the area of their feet also presents problems for students. Since they drew their feet on blank paper, the first thing they need to figure out is what square units they will use. Students might try the color tiles, pattern blocks, or cubes. If they do so, ask whether they have accounted for all the space (gaps), or what they are doing about the pieces that hang over the outline of their feet. Again, one or two students should figure out that if they traced their feet on grid paper, they would then have squares to count. If no student brings this up, present the idea yourself. The Three-Fourths-Inch Grid Paper (M18) or Centimeter Grid Paper (M19) may be used.

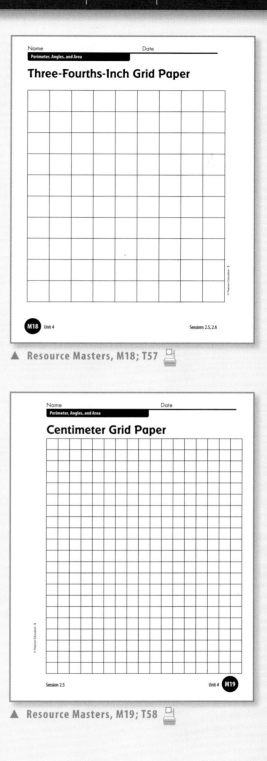

▲ Resource Masters, M18; T57

▲ Resource Masters, M19; T58

Teaching Note

② How Much Accuracy Do We Expect? One purpose of this activity is to reinforce the need to account for all of the space when determining area. Measuring the area of an irregular shape like a footprint creates challenges since the partial units are not easily identified as "half" or "whole" units like the triangles that students worked with in the tetromino activities. Therefore, for the purposes of this activity, it is sufficient for students to approximate the whole units formed by combining the partial units within the footprints. Similarly, do not expect complete accuracy in finding the perimeter of the footprint; instead focus the activity and subsequent discussion on appropriate tools to account for the full length of the perimeter.

Students use grid paper to determine the area of their feet.

Using grid paper to determine the area of their feet also presents challenges. What do they do with the partial pieces? Do they ignore them? Count them as one? Combine them in some way?②

ONGOING ASSESSMENT: Observing Students at Work

Students find the perimeter and area of an irregular shape.

- **Do students know which measurement is area and which is perimeter?**

- **How do students determine the perimeter?** Are they using an appropriate tool?

- **How do students determine the area?** Are they aware they need to use a standard unit?

- **Do students know that they have to account for all the space inside the foot, and not just the full squares?** Do they combine partial units to create square units?

- **Are students counting by ones when they find the measurements?** Are they using a larger unit (e.g., finding a rectangle within their footprint and counting by rows or columns)?

- **How do students record their measurements?** Do they use the correct labels (e.g., inches or centimeters for perimeter, square units for area)?

3 DISCUSSION
What's the Area?

10 MIN   CLASS   PAIRS

Math Focus Points for Discussion

◆ Finding the area of partially covered rectangles

Have students share with a partner their answer for Problem 1 on *Student Activity Book* page 29 and how they determined the area. Give students a minute or two to do this.

Who is willing to explain their thinking to the whole class?

Have several students explain their thinking on how they determined the area of the entire rectangle. Possible strategies include

- Drawing grid lines over the "rug," and then counting all the squares, by either counting by ones, skip counting, or multiplying.

- Selecting one column and one row where they can see all of the squares, and counting by ones or skip counting

Ask each student who shares:

How did you decide how many squares were covered by the rug? How did you count all the squares?

Some students realize that they can count the rows or the columns. Encourage students to be thinking about counting by more than one unit at a time.

If time allows, you may choose to discuss another problem on the page.

---

4 SESSION FOLLOW-UP
Daily Practice

 Daily Practice: For reinforcement of this unit's content, have students complete *Student Activity Book* page 34.

 Student Math Handbook: Students and families may use *Student Math Handbook* pages 112–113, 114, 115 for reference and review. See pages 160–164 in the back of this unit.

Name _____ Date _____

Perimeter, Angles, and Area   Daily Practice

Seven-Unit Shapes

Use the Square and Triangle Cutouts (M17) to make three new shapes with an area of seven square units. Remember that each new shape must, like tetrominoes, have full sides touching.

NOTE Students build shapes with an area of 7 square units.

115

Tape or glue the new shapes you make on a large piece of paper. You may also draw the new shapes.

1. Use only squares in your first shape.

2. Use only triangles in your second shape.

3. Use both squares and triangles in your third shape.

Ongoing Review

4. What is the area of the following shape?

A. 2 square units   **C.** $3\frac{1}{2}$ square units

B. 3 square units   **D.** 4 square units

34 Unit 4   Session 2.5

▲ **Student Activity Book, p. 34**

Assessment: Make a Shape

Math Focus Points

◆ Designing a shape for a given area

◆ Finding area by counting or calculating whole and partial square units

◆ Finding the perimeter of an irregular shape

◆ Finding the area of an irregular shape

Today's Plan		Materials
① ASSESSMENT ACTIVITY **Make a Shape** ✔ 🕐 15 MIN 🚶 INDIVIDUALS		• M20*
② MATH WORKSHOP **Finding Area** **2A** *Shape Poster* **2B** *What's the Area?* **2C** *How Big Is Your Foot?* **2D** *LogoPaths* Activity: *500 Steps* (optional) 🕐 30 MIN		**2A** • Materials from Session 2.4, p. 81 **2B** • Materials from Session 2.4, p. 81 **2C** • Materials from Session 2.5, p. 88 **2D** • M6*
③ DISCUSSION **Perimeter and Area** 🕐 15 MIN 👥 CLASS		
④ SESSION FOLLOW-UP **Daily Practice and Homework**		• *Student Activity Book,* pp. 35–36 • *Student Math Handbook,* pp. 112–113, 114, 115

*See *Materials to Prepare,* p. 61.

Ten-Minute Math

Quick Images: 2–D Show Images 9 and 10 (one at a time) from *Quick Images: 2-D* (T53) and follow the procedure for the basic routine. For each image, students discuss how they drew their figures, including any revisions they made after each viewing.

Ask students:

• How did you remember the parts of the image?

• What did you notice about the relationship of the parts of the image?

• What helped you remember the whole image, so you could draw your design?

ASSESSMENT ACTIVITY
Make a Shape

15 MIN   INDIVIDUALS

On Assessment: Make a Shape (M20), students are asked to create a shape with a given area (5–7 square units) on dot paper and then explain how they determined the area.

This problem addresses Benchmark 2: Identify and find the area of given figures by counting whole and partial square units.

Once students have finished with the assessment, they continue Math Workshop activities.

ONGOING ASSESSMENT: Observing Students at Work

Students create a shape with a given area and justify their solution.

- **Do students accurately create shapes with an area of 5, 6, or 7 square units on the dot paper?**

- **Are their shapes composed of both triangles and squares?**

- **Do their explanations of how they determined the area demonstrate understanding of how much area the half and whole unit triangles cover (that the smaller triangle is equal to $\frac{1}{2}$ a square unit and the larger triangle is equal to 1 square unit)?❶ ❷**

MATH WORKSHOP
Finding Area

30 MIN

Students use the third day of Math Workshop to complete all the activities. Only students who have not yet finished their Shape Posters should spend any time on that activity. Consider creating a display to exhibit the completed Shape Posters. Make sure students measure the perimeter and area of their feet before the end of Math Workshop, as they will discuss their solutions at the end of the session.

Students who have time can work on the *LogoPaths* activity, *500 Steps*. If they did not work on *200 Steps* and *400 Steps* in the previous Math Workshops, they should complete those activities before moving on to *500 Steps*.

Spend a few minutes checking in with students and make certain they know what tasks they are expected to finish.

Professional Development

❶ **Teacher Note:** Assessment: Make a Shape, p. 145

Differentiation

❷ **English Language Learners** If some English Language Learners are unable to write their explanations in English, it may be possible in some classrooms to give them the option of responding in their native languages. You can also look at the shapes together and ask guided questions to help students who are not yet able to write in English to explain their thinking while you jot down their responses.
How many square units are in your shape? Can you count them for me? Can you point to all the parts of your shape that are equal to 1 square unit? to $\frac{1}{2}$ a square unit?

Name _____ Date _____

Perimeter, Angles, and Area

Assessment: Make a Shape

Make a shape with an area of 5, 6, or 7 square units. Draw it on the dot grid. Use both squares and triangles in your shape.

What is the area of your shape? _____
Write how you know that your shape has that area.

M20 Unit 4   Session 2.6

▲ **Resource Masters, M20**

Name   Date

Perimeter, Angles, and Area

LogoPaths: 500 Steps

Use *LogoPaths Free Explore* to make rectangles with perimeters of 500 turtle steps. Make sure that some of your rectangles have sides that are not multiples of 10. If you can, make a square with a perimeter of 500 steps. Use the **Teach** tool to name your solutions. Save your work when you have finished.

Sketch at least four of the rectangles you made in the space below. Label the length of each side.

M6   Unit 4

▲ **Resource Masters, M6**

2A *Shape Poster*

For details about this activity, see Session 2.4, page 83.

2B What's the Area?

For details about this activity, see Session 2.4, page 84.

2C How Big Is Your Foot?

Students will need time to find the area and perimeter of their footprints. If students seem uncertain how to find the perimeter or area, consider having small group (or even whole class) discussions where students share strategies they have been using.

Students might say:

"To find the perimeter, I used a piece of yarn to go around my footprint. I stretched out the yarn, then used the ruler to measure how long the perimeter was."

"I wanted to find the area so I traced my foot again using grid paper. Then I counted the squares. It got hard, though, when there were just pieces of squares."

For details about this activity, see Session 2.5, page 90.

2D *LogoPaths* Activity: *500 Steps*

Students who completed the *200 Steps* and *400 Steps* activities in the previous Math Workshops can move on to *500 Steps*, following the same procedure as the *200 Steps* activity. Using the *LogoPaths* software, they build as many rectangles as they can with a perimeter of 500 steps. They record the commands they used and choose four rectangles to sketch and label on *LogoPaths: 500 Steps* (M6).

For details about this activity, see Session 2.4, page 84.

DISCUSSION

③ Perimeter and Area

15 MIN   CLASS

Math Focus Points for Discussion

◆ Finding the perimeter of an irregular shape ④

◆ Finding the area of an irregular shape

Start the discussion by asking students to share with partners how they found the perimeter of their feet. Give them a few minutes to do this.

Who wants to explain how you found the perimeter of your foot? What made it hard to find the perimeter?

Have several students explain their strategies for finding perimeter.

So in the end, most of you used a ruler or meterstick to measure the yarn or string you used to find the perimeter, the length of the distance around your foot. Now, talk to a partner about how you found the area of your foot.

Give students time to talk to a partner.

Who wants to explain how you found the area of your foot? . . . What made it hard to find the area?

Have several students explain their strategy for finding area.

We can see that we used different ways to measure the perimeter and area. For perimeter we used a ruler or meterstick, and for area we had to use some kind of square unit.

SESSION FOLLOW-UP

④ Daily Practice and Homework

  Daily Practice: For ongoing review, have students complete *Student Activity Book* page 35.

  Homework: Students practice making rectangles and squares with given perimeters on *Student Activity Book* page 36.

Student Math Handbook: Students and families may use *Student Math Handbook* pages 112–113, 114, 115 for reference and review. See pages 160–164 in the back of this unit.

Professional Development

④ **Dialogue Box:** Finding Perimeter and Area, p. 156

Name _____ Date _____
Perimeter, Angles, and Area   Daily Practice

How Many 10s?
Solve each problem below. You may use your 1,000 chart to help you. Explain how you figured out each problem.

NOTE Students find groups of 10s in 3-digit numbers.
6, 7–8

1. Mr. Jackson went to Sticker Station and bought strips of 10 stickers to give to his students. He bought 270 stickers. How many strips of 10 did he buy?

2. Ms. Donaldson's class has collected 375 stamps from old letters. They are displaying the stamps in rows of 10. How many rows can they make? How many stamps will be left over?

3. Ms. Vega's class is collecting bottle caps. They are displaying them in stacks of 10. So far they have 41 stacks of bottle caps and 3 single bottle caps. How many bottle caps do they have?

4. Philip and his sister are collecting pennies at home. They have 256 pennies so far. If they trade the pennies for dimes, how many dimes will they have? How many pennies will be left over?

Session 2.6   Unit 4   35

▲ **Student Activity Book, p. 35**

Name _____ Date _____
Perimeter, Angles, and Area   Homework

More Perimeter Problems

1. Draw at least two different rectangles, each with a perimeter of 160 units. Label the length of each side.

NOTE Students practice making rectangles and squares that have given perimeters.
112–113

2. My perimeter is 200. The length of one of my sides is 75. Draw the rest of my sides to make me a whole rectangle. Label the length of each side.

75

36   Unit 4   Session 2.6

▲ **Student Activity Book, p. 36**

Mathematical Emphases

Features of Shape Describing and classifying
2-dimensional figures

Math Focus Points

◆ Identifying the attributes of triangles: three sides, three vertices, and three angles

◆ Identifying the attributes of quadrilaterals: four sides, four vertices, and four angles

◆ Comparing the properties of squares and rectangles

◆ Determining the geometric moves needed (slides, flips, turns) to prove or disprove congruence between two shapes.

Features of Shape Describing and measuring angles

Math Focus Points

◆ Recognizing right angles

◆ Identifying a right angle as having a measure of 90 degrees

◆ Understanding angle size as the degree of turn

◆ Comparing the sizes of angles

Triangles, Quadrilaterals, and Angles

SESSION 3.1 p. 104	Student Activity Book	Student Math Handbook	Professional Development: Read Ahead of Time
Triangles Students build triangles and consider the attributes that make them triangles.	37–39	120, 122–123	• **Teacher Note:** Beyond Vocabulary, p. 148
SESSION 3.2 p. 110			
Is It a Triangle? Students identify shapes that are and are not triangles. They discuss whether or not any three-sided closed figure can be a triangle.	40–44	120	• **Dialogue Box:** Building a Definition of Triangles, p. 158
SESSION 3.3 p. 116			
Squares, Rectangles, and Other Quadrilaterals Students use building kits to make quadrilaterals, including some with angles other than right angles. They discuss the relationship between squares and rectangles.	45–48	121, 122–123	
SESSION 3.4 p. 123			
Angles of Different Sizes Students consider sizes of angles relative to right angles, or 90 degrees. They find examples of different-sized angles around the classroom.	49–51	122–123	

Ten-Minute Math See page 16 for an overview.

Quick Images: 2-D

- T53–T54, *Quick Images: 2-D* 🖥
  (Images 11–16)

Practicing Place Value

- **No materials needed**

Materials to Gather	Materials to Prepare
• **Straw Building Kits** (1 kit per 6 students) • **Triangles** (made by students)	• **Straw Building Kits** If you are not using purchased straw building kits, you can make building kits from plastic drinking straws or thin dowels. For each kit, you will need the following quantities of each of these lengths: 10 eight-inch lengths, 10 six-inch lengths, 20 five-inch lengths, 20 four-inch lengths, 15 three-inch lengths, 10 two-inch lengths. For connectors, you can use clay, homemade or commercial play dough, styrofoam or florist's foam. If you are using hollow straws, you can also use twist ties, paper clips, or pipe cleaners, bent and stuck inside the straw ends to connect two straws together. Each kit should include enough material for about 20 connectors. You will need one building kit for every 6 students. You will use these building kits again in the 3-D Geometry unit, *Solids and Boxes,* later in the year. • **Chart paper** Label the chart paper "Triangles Have . . ."
• **T59, Tricky Triangles** 🖥 • **Computers with** *LogoPaths* **software installed**	
• **Straw Building Kits** (1 kit per 6 students) • **Computers with** *LogoPaths* **software installed** • **Squares and rectangles** (made by students)	• **Chart paper** Label the chart paper "Squares and Rectangles." Label subheadings "Same" and "Different."
• **2 straws and 1 flexible connector** (per pair)	• **Straw Building Kit** Make a sample 4″ x 8″ rectangle. • **Flexible connector** Make a sample moveable angle using 2 straws and 1 connector.

🖥 Overhead Transparency

Triangles, Quadrilaterals, and Angles, *continued*

	Student Activity Book	Student Math Handbook	Professional Development: Read Ahead of Time	
SESSION 3.5 p. 129				
Working With Shapes and Angles Students continue to explore the characteristics of triangles, quadrilaterals, and angles, including angle measurement.	37–38, 45–46, 49–50, 52–55	120, 121, 122–123		
SESSION 3.6 p. 134				
End-of-Unit Assessment Students complete assessment tasks that focus on finding and identifying area, triangles, and right angles.	57	115, 120, 121, 122–123	• **Teacher Note:** End-of-Unit Assessment, p. 149	

Materials to Gather	Materials to Prepare
• **2 straws and 1 flexible connector** (per pair) • **Straw building kits** (1 kit per 6 students) • **Computers with** *LogoPaths* **software installed**	• **Chart paper** Label the chart paper "Different-Sized Angles." Subheadings are labeled as follows: "Less than 90 degrees; 90 degrees; Greater than 90 degrees."
	• **M22–M24, End-of-Unit Assessment** Make 1 copy per student.

Triangles

Math Focus Points

- Identifying the attributes of triangles: three sides, three vertices, and three angles
- Recognizing right angles

Vocabulary

vertex (vertices)
right angle

Today's Plan			Materials
1 ACTIVITY **Introducing Building Triangles**	10 MIN	CLASS	• Straw Building Kits*
2 ACTIVITY **Building Triangles**	30 MIN	PAIRS	• *Student Activity Book,* pp. 37–38 • Straw Building Kits
3 DISCUSSION **Attributes of Triangles**	20 MIN	CLASS	• Chart: "Triangles Have. . ."*; triangles (made by students)
4 SESSION FOLLOW-UP **Daily Practice**			• *Student Activity Book,* p. 39 • *Student Math Handbook,* pp. 120, 122–123

*See *Materials to Prepare,* p. 101.

Ten-Minute Math

***Quick Images:* 2-D** Show Images 11 and 12 (one at a time) from *Quick Images: 2-D* (T53) and follow the procedure for the basic routine. For each image, students discuss how they drew their figures, including any revisions they made after each viewing. Ask students:

- How did you remember the parts of the image?
- What did you notice about the relationship of the parts of the image?
- What helped you remember the whole image, so you could draw your design?

ACTIVITY

① Introducing Building Triangles

10 MIN   CLASS

Begin this session by introducing students to the Straw Building Kits. Point out that each kit has straws that come in different lengths, which can be connected to make a variety of shapes. Let them know that they will be using these materials to make shapes that they are already familiar with from their work in earlier grades—triangles (in this session) and quadrilaterals (in Session 3.3).

Who can tell us how many sides a triangle has? . . . Can someone come up and draw a triangle for us?

Choose two or three students to each draw a triangle on the board or overhead. Use these drawings to remind students about some of the characteristics of triangles and other shapes.

We call the straight parts of a shape like a triangle the "sides." The corners where two sides meet are called "vertices," or if you're talking about just one corner, we use the word "vertex." How many vertices does a triangle have?

Point to some examples of sides and vertices and write these words next to the drawings.❶ ❷

Now demonstrate how to build a triangle using three straws of different lengths, such as a 5-inch, 6-inch, and 8-inch straw. Show students how to use the connectors.

A teacher demonstrates how twist ties and straws can be joined to form triangles.

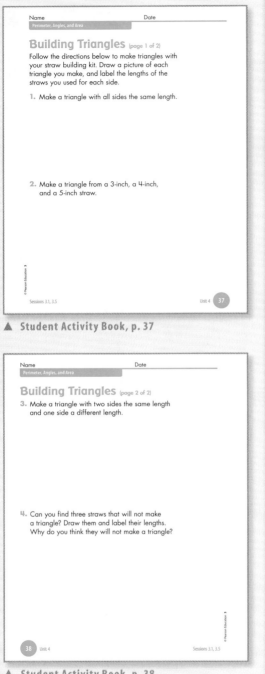

▲ Student Activity Book, p. 37

▲ Student Activity Book, p. 38

Here's one kind of triangle I can make with the straws. Your job today will be to build a few different triangles. You will use different lengths of straws, and see how that changes the shape of the triangles you build. We'll share some of your triangles when we come back together later.

ACTIVITY

2 Building Triangles

30 MIN   PAIRS

Students build triangles using the materials in the straw building kits. They work in pairs, with three pairs of students sharing one building kit. Have students draw illustrations to record their work on *Student Activity Book* pages 37–38. Since there is no room for students to actually trace their triangles on the *Student Activity Book* page, let them know that they should draw a smaller picture that matches the shape they built. To have enough straws, students may have to take some figures apart to build new triangles. Be sure to save examples of triangles for each problem for the discussion at the end of the session.

Students work in pairs to build triangles using the straw kit.

ONGOING ASSESSMENT: Observing Students at Work

Students build triangles using straws for sides and connectors for vertices.

- **Are students able to build triangles according to the given constraints?** When they draw these triangles, do they pay attention to the lengths of the sides and try to approximate these? Are they beginning to pay attention to angle size, and approximate these as well?

- **Are students able to identify three lengths that will not make a triangle?**

As students build and then draw their triangles, ask questions to draw their attention to how the lengths of the sides affect the shape of the different triangles they build, such as:

For Problems 1 and 2

- What do you notice about the shape of the triangle you made with straws that are all the same length and the triangle you made with straws of different lengths? How are they different? How are they the same?

For Problems 3 and 4

- When you chose your two straws that are the same, could you have chosen any other straw for the third side as long as it was different? What size straws worked to make a triangle? What sizes didn't work? Why do you think that is?

DIFFERENTIATION: Supporting the Range of Learners

Intervention If some students are having difficulty drawing the figures accurately, suggest that they trace the straw triangles onto a larger piece of blank paper.

ELL You may wish to meet with English Language Learners ahead of time to review vocabulary that they will need to describe the straws and the shapes they use to build triangles.

Extension Students who are ready to be challenged can explore the idea that a particular set of sides that makes a triangle cannot make a triangle with a different shape. You might ask:

- How many triangles can you make with a 5-inch, 6-inch, and 8-inch straw? Why do you think it's only that many?

DISCUSSION

③ Attributes of Triangles

20 MIN   CLASS

Math Focus Points for Discussion

◆ Identifying the attributes of triangles: three sides, three vertices, and three angles

◆ Recognizing right angles

Show students the chart you prepared titled "Triangles Have . . .".

What are some things you noticed about all the triangles you made today? What's the same about them?

Students should be able to say that they all have three sides and three vertices (which students may still refer to as "corners"). Write these on the chart. Some students may also say that triangles have three angles. Ask one or two students to show you where the angles are in one of the triangles they made.

Point to one of the vertices in your triangle. Now show us where the angle is. Can you trace it with your finger? . . . Can you show us another angle in the same triangle? . . . How many angles are there altogether? . . . Does every triangle you made have three angles?

Once students agree that each of their triangles has exactly three angles, add this to the chart.

> Triangles Have . . .
>
> Three sides.
>
> Three vertices.
>
> Three angles.

Now ask two or three students to show their triangles for Problem 2 (using a 3-inch, a 4-inch, and a 5-inch straw that make a right triangle).

What do you notice about these triangles?

Students may notice that the triangles are the same size and shape. Show how one will fit over the other exactly and remind students about the term "congruent."

When two shapes fit exactly like this, or when one is a copy of the other, we use the word "congruent." These two triangles are exactly the same size and same shape, so they are congruent.

If students do not mention that the triangle has a right angle, call their attention to this.

Look at this angle in the triangle. This angle is like the angles in rectangles. Who remembers what this kind of angle is called?

Students have heard the term "right angle" in Grade 2; however, if no one responds, tell them that this is the name for angles like this, which are also like the corners of a piece of paper. Hold up a piece of blank paper to make this point.

This is another **right angle**. What about the other angles in the triangle? Do you think they are greater or less than a right angle?

Move the triangle around so that the other angles can be seen in different positions. Let the students think about your questions. Solicit a few student responses, but do not have a lengthy discussion. At this point, just raise the idea about angles for them to think about. Students will be doing more work with angles as this investigation continues.

Finish the discussion about triangles by asking students if they found any lengths that did not make a triangle (Problem 4). Students will likely say things such as, "You can't have two short sides and one that's longer than the short ones put together." This is true. If one side is longer than the sum of the lengths of the other two, a triangle cannot be made. Collect a couple of examples of lengths that students found did not make triangles.

Post the "Triangles Have. . ." chart where students can refer to it as they continue to work on shapes and angles.

▲ **Student Activity Book, p. 39**

SESSION FOLLOW-UP
4 Daily Practice

 Daily Practice: For ongoing review, have students complete *Student Activity Book* page 39.

 Student Math Handbook: Students and families may use *Student Math Handbook* pages 120, 122–123 for reference and review. See pages 160–164 in the back of this unit.

Is It a Triangle?

Math Focus Points

◆ Identifying the attributes of triangles: three sides, three vertices, and three angles

Today's Plan		Materials
ACTIVITY **① Tricky Triangles**	30 MIN PAIRS INDIVIDUALS	• *Student Activity Book*, pp. 40–42
DISCUSSION **② What's a Triangle?**	30 MIN CLASS	• T59
ACTIVITY **③ Introducing *LogoPaths*: *Feed the Turtle* (optional)**	CLASS GROUPS	• Computers with *LogoPaths* software installed
SESSION FOLLOW-UP **④ Daily Practice and Homework**		• *Student Activity Book*, pp. 43–44 • *Student Math Handbook*, p. 120

Ten-Minute Math

Practicing Place Value Write 602 on the board and have students practice saying it to a partner. Make sure all students can read, write, and say this number correctly.

Ask students:

• Find and sketch five or six different ways to make 602 using only sheets of 100, strips of 10, and single stickers (such as 6 sheets, 2 singles or 3 sheets, 30 strips, and 2 singles).

Collect a few examples on the board and ask students how they found their answers. Did anyone notice a pattern?

ACTIVITY
1 Tricky Triangles

30 MIN PAIRS INDIVIDUALS

Students work individually and then with a partner to examine a set of shapes to determine if they are triangles or not. They first look at the shapes on *Student Activity Book* page 40, and decide which of the figures are triangles and which are not. They record their thinking on *Student Activity Book* page 41.

Students compare their lists with a partner and discuss any differences.

The non-triangular shapes include figures that are not closed, that have curved sides, and that have more than three sides. The triangular shapes include some that students might be reluctant to consider as triangles: some that have very small or very large angles, that have sides of very different lengths, or that are oriented without a horizontal base.

ONGOING ASSESSMENT: Observing Students at Work

Students examine a set of shapes to determine which are triangles and which are not.

- **Do students recognize that triangles must have three sides, three vertices, and three angles?**

- **Do students recognize that triangles can be oriented in many ways?**

- **Do students recognize that triangles may have angles that are the same size or very different sizes from one another?**

Name _____ **Date** _____

Perimeter, Angles, and Area

Tricky Triangles

A B C D E F G H I J M K L N O P

40 Unit 4 | Session 3.2

▲ **Student Activity Book, p. 40;**
Resource Masters, M21; T59

Name _____ **Date** _____

Perimeter, Angles, and Area

Which Are Triangles? (page 1 of 2)

1. Which of the Tricky Triangles on page 40 are actually triangles? Without showing your partner, list the letter of each shape in the box below where you think it belongs.

These shapes are triangles:	These shapes are **not** triangles:

2. Now compare your list with your partner's. Discuss any shapes on which you disagree.

3. After you have discussed the Tricky Triangles with your partner, write why you think certain shapes are triangles and others are not triangles.

Session 3.2 | Unit 4 41

▲ **Student Activity Book, p. 41** WRITING

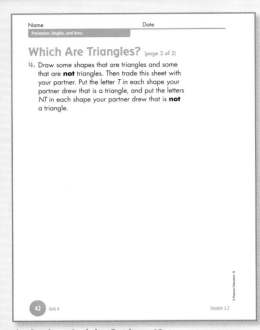

Name _____ Date _____

Perimeter, Angles, and Area

Which Are Triangles? (page 2 of 2)

4. Draw some shapes that are triangles and some that are **not** triangles. Then trade this sheet with your partner. Put the letter *T* in each shape your partner drew that is a triangle, and put the letters *NT* in each shape your partner drew that is **not** a triangle.

42 Unit 4   Session 3.2

▲ **Student Activity Book, p. 42**

DIFFERENTIATION: Supporting the Range of Learners

Intervention If some students are having difficulty identifying as triangles shapes that are not oriented with a horizontal base, ask them what would happen if they turned the paper until the triangle looks more familiar:

● Does turning the paper change the shape?

You can also remind them to check if the shape has all of the properties of a triangle.

● Is it a closed shape? Does it have three straight sides? Does it have three angles?

You can also invite students to express their reservations.

● Why doesn't it seem like a triangle to you?

DISCUSSION

2 What's a Triangle?

30 MIN   CLASS

Math Focus Points for Discussion

◆ Identifying the attributes of triangles: three sides, three vertices, and three angles

Have students bring *Student Activity Book* pages 40–42 to the discussion. Display the transparency of Tricky Triangles (T59) on the overhead.

Let's start by talking about a shape that was confusing or difficult to think about. Maybe it seemed like it shouldn't be a triangle at first, but then you decided it was.

Look for ways to bring up the following points:

● Shapes A, C, H, and M may not seem to be triangles because they are not oriented with a horizontal base. Focus the discussion on the fact that if you move the paper around, or cut out the shapes and move them, you can make the shapes look more familiar.

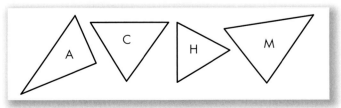

- Shapes O and F may not seem to be triangles because their sides and angles are different from each other as compared to the more familiar shape of an equilateral triangle which has equal sides and equal angles. Shapes O and F also both contain angles greater than 90°, which students are also unaccustomed to seeing. Focus the discussion on the fact that these shapes have three sides and three angles, which is what makes each a triangle.

Professional Development

❶ **Dialogue Box:** Building a Definition of Triangles, p. 158

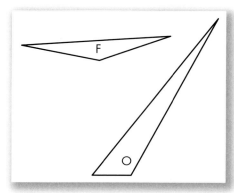

After students have discussed some of these shapes, ask about shapes that are on their "not triangles" list.

Are there some shapes on your "not triangles" list that tricked you at first? Are there some that seemed like they might be triangles?

Students might offer shapes P and B as examples that are "almost" triangles but are not because they are not closed. Shapes E, G, and K are close to a triangular shape, but some sides are curved and not line segments. Shapes D and I also look "triangular," but they have four sides. Shapes L and N are not polygons because their segments cross each other.

Students do not need to address every shape on the list, as long as the points about what makes a shape a triangle are included. However, if one of the points above is not included, you should ask about a shape that illustrates that idea. For instance, if no student brings up the idea that a triangle does not have curved sides, ask about how they categorized shape K to call attention to that idea.❶

ACTIVITY

CLASS GROUPS

③ Introducing *LogoPaths: Feed the Turtle* (optional)

In this *LogoPaths* activity, students move a turtle through a maze to collect food at various locations. To move the turtle, they use forward (**FD**) and backward (**BK**) moves in multiples of 10 and right (**RT**) and left (**LT**) turns in multiples of 30 degrees. This game helps students develop familiarity with degrees as a way of measuring turns—for example, a quarter turn is 90 degrees, a half turn or reverse in direction is 180 degrees, and so on. The activity also helps them develop and compare visual images of different turning angles.

Open *Feed the Turtle* in the *LogoPaths* software, and select the Level 1 game.

In this game, your job is to help the turtle get to the food in the maze before it runs out of energy. Every time the turtle eats, it fills up its energy supply. You want to have enough energy to get to the next prize and to finish the game, so make sure you carefully plan the order in which the turtle eats the food.

In this activity, you can only use multiples of 10 for all of the forward and back moves. For all of the right and left turns, you can only use multiples of 30. Remember, multiples of 10 are the numbers you land on if you count by 10. Multiples of 30 are the numbers you land on if you count by 30. So when the turtle needs to turn, you can turn it left or right 30, 60, 90, 120, and so on.

Generate a few more multiples of 30 and list them (starting with 30) on the board. Then, using students' suggestions for the forward distance, move the turtle to the first turn in the *Feed the Turtle* maze. Point out the importance of being in the middle of an intersection before making a turn in order to avoid running into a wall. Although estimation combined with trial and error is a good method of finding the distances the turtle needs to move, you can also show students how to use the Ruler❷ tool to measure the distance from the turtle to where they want the turtle to go.

When you play *Get the Toys,* you can only turn right or left 90 degrees. When you play *Feed the Turtle,* you have more options. You can turn 90 degrees or you can turn more or less than 90 degrees by typing in multiples of 30.

Look at where the turtle is in the maze. It needs to turn right to get the food, so I'm going to type in the command for a right turn [type **RT**]. Does the turtle need to turn right more than 90 degrees or less than 90 degrees? Remember: You can only use multiples of 30, like 30, 60, 90, 120, and so on.

Elicit student suggestions and demonstrate them on the computer (such as **RT 30** or **RT 60**).

Many of you thought that we needed to turn the turtle 30 degrees, when the turn was actually 60 degrees. Don't worry if you're not getting the correct turns right away. You'll get better at being able to identify the turning angle the more you play this and other *LogoPath* games.

Show students how to use the Turtle Turner❷ tool.

If you really feel stuck, you can use the Turtle Turner tool to help you. However, you should always try to figure out the turning angle yourself before using this tool. And remember, the more you play, the better you'll get.

SESSION FOLLOW-UP

Daily Practice and Homework

 Daily Practice: For reinforcement of this unit's content, have students complete *Student Activity Book* page 43.

Homework: Students solve sets of related addition and subtraction problems on *Student Activity Book* page 44.

Student Math Handbook: Students and families may use *Student Math Handbook* page 120 for reference and review. See pages 160–164 in the back of this unit.

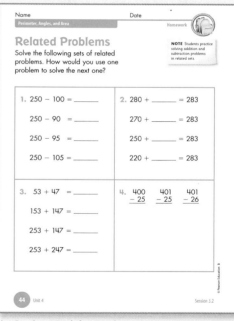

▲ **Student Activity Book, p. 43**

▲ **Student Activity Book, p. 44**

Squares, Rectangles, and Other Quadrilaterals

Math Focus Points

◆ Identifying the attributes of quadrilaterals: four sides, four vertices, and four angles

◆ Comparing the properties of squares and rectangles

◆ Identifying a right angle as having a measure of 90 degrees

Vocabulary

quadrilateral
degree

Today's Plan		Materials
① ACTIVITY **Introducing Building Quadrilaterals**	10 MIN CLASS	• Straw Building Kit
② MATH WORKSHOP **Building Quadrilaterals** **2A** Building Quadrilaterals **2B** *LogoPaths* Activity: *Feed the Turtle*	35 MIN	**2A** • *Student Activity Book,* pp. 45–46 • Straw Building Kits **2B** • Computers with *LogoPaths* software installed
③ DISCUSSION **Squares and Rectangles**	15 MIN CLASS	• Squares and rectangles (made by student) • Chart: "Squares and Rectangles"*
④ SESSION FOLLOW-UP **Daily Practice and Homework**		• *Student Activity Book,* pp. 47–48 • *Student Math Handbook,* pp. 121, 122–123

*See *Materials to Prepare,* p. 101.

Ten-Minute Math

Quick Images: 2-D Show Images 13 and 14 (one at a time) from *Quick Images: 2-D* (T54) and follow the procedure for the basic routine. For each image, students discuss how they drew their figures, including any revisions they made after each viewing.

Ask students:

• How did you remember the parts of the image?

• What did you notice about the relationship of the parts of the image?

• What helped you remember the whole image, so you could draw your design?

ACTIVITY

1 Introducing Building Quadrilaterals

 10 MIN CLASS

Begin this session by reminding students of their work on quadrilaterals in previous grades.

The other day you used the materials in the building kits to build triangles. Today you will use them to make another kind of figure called a **quadrilateral**. *Who remembers what a quadrilateral is? . . . How many sides does a quadrilateral have? . . . Can anyone name a shape that is a quadrilateral, that is, a shape that has four sides?*

Ask a couple of students to draw a square and a rectangle on the board or overhead.

Where are the sides in each of these figures? . . . Where are the vertices? . . . How many vertices are there in each of these figures? . . . What do you notice about the angles in these figures?

Students should notice that all the squares and rectangles have right angles (even though it is likely that the angles in students' drawings may not be exactly "square"). If they do not, however, leave this as a question for them to consider as they're building. This will be part of the discussion at the end of the session.❶

Are there any other shapes you can think of that have four sides and four vertices, but are not squares or rectangles?

Students may think of other quadrilaterals that they are familiar with from the set of pattern blocks, trapezoids, and rhombuses. Draw examples of these or other quadrilaterals that students suggest.

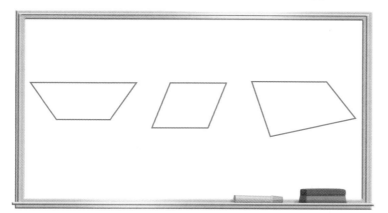

Tell students that when they build their own quadrilaterals, they can make different sizes of squares and rectangles. They should also try to make shapes that have four sides but are not squares or rectangles.

Math Note

❶ **Squares, Rectangles, and Right Angles** At this point, not all students may be able to define squares and rectangles as having right angles, even though they recognize these visually as "square corners." For example, if a square is rotated so that it sits on one vertex, third graders may argue that it is not a square because it does not look like their idea of a square as sitting on one side. They might also say that the angle also does not look like a right angle. This is an idea that students need time to develop and discuss with a variety of shapes, as you may have noted when students discussed the orientation of triangles in the previous session.

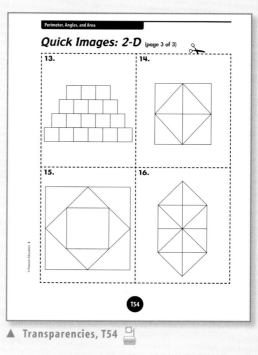

▲ Transparencies, T54

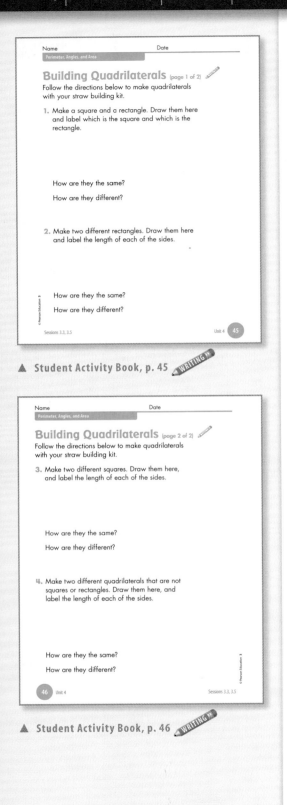

▲ Student Activity Book, p. 45

▲ Student Activity Book, p. 46

MATH WORKSHOP

② Building Quadrilaterals

35 MIN

In this Math Workshop, students work on building quadrilaterals and the *LogoPaths* activity, *Feed the Turtle*. All students should complete Problem 1 on *Student Activity Book* page 45, before going on to the *LogoPaths* activity, so that they can participate in the discussion. They will have more time to work on building quadrilaterals in Session 3.5.

②A Building Quadrilaterals

PAIRS

Students work in pairs to build quadrilaterals, using the straw building kits, and examine the relationship between rectangles and squares. They record their work on *Student Activity Book* pages 45–46.

Students use the straw building kits to build quadrilaterals.

ONGOING ASSESSMENT: Observing Students at Work

Students build squares, rectangles, and other quadrilaterals, and compare these to one another.

- **Do students choose correct side lengths to make squares?** To make rectangles?

- **Do students recognize that both squares and rectangles have right angles?**

- **Are students able to build quadrilaterals that are not squares or rectangles?**

DIFFERENTIATION: Supporting the Range of Learners

Extension Students who could use a challenge can work on making quadrilaterals from four different lengths: eight inches, six inches, five inches, and four inches.

- How many different quadrilaterals can you make from these four straws? How do you know they are different?

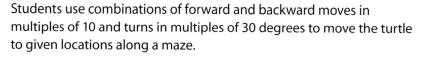

2B *LogoPaths* Activity: *Feed the Turtle*

PAIRS   INDIVIDUALS

Students work alone or with partners on this *LogoPaths* activity in which they use *LogoPaths* commands to move a turtle to given locations within a maze in order to get food. The turtle gets more energy each time it reaches food. To move the turtle, students use a combination of forward and backward moves in multiples of 10 and turns in multiples of 30 degrees.

ONGOING ASSESSMENT: Observing Students at Work

Students use combinations of forward and backward moves in multiples of 10 and turns in multiples of 30 degrees to move the turtle to given locations along a maze.

- **Can students use *LogoPaths* commands fluently?**

- **Do they use right and left turns consistently even when the turtle is not facing straight up?**

- **Do students recognize a turn of 90 degrees?** Are students able to accurately determine other turning angles (30 degrees, 60 degrees, 150 degrees)?

- **Can students visualize the commands needed to move the turtle toward the desired locations?** Do they move one command at a time or are they able to write several commands on a single line?

- **How do they generate commands to reverse a path?** Do they back up the same distance that they went forward? Do they use a turn in the opposite direction? For example, if they turned **RT 60**, do they now turn **LT 60** to reverse direction? Do they use a turn of 180° to reverse direction?

15 MIN   CLASS

DISCUSSION

③ Squares and Rectangles

Math Focus Points for Discussion

◆ Comparing the properties of squares and rectangles

◆ Identifying a right angle as having a measure of 90 degrees

Bring the class together and ask students to share the squares and rectangles they built for Problem 1. Choose several squares and several rectangles of different sizes to display; be sure at least two of the rectangles also have differently proportioned widths and heights.

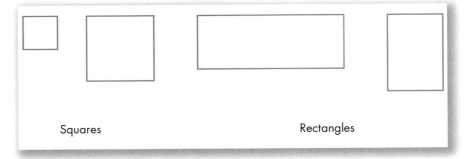

Squares   Rectangles

What is the same about all of these squares and rectangles?

As students tell you their ideas, list these on the chart you prepared, in the column labeled "Same." This list should include the fact that each of these figures has four sides, four vertices, corners, or angles, and that opposite pairs of sides have the same length. Students may also say that each figure has four right angles. If this does not come up, ask again what students noticed about the angles.

Squares and Rectangles	
<u>Same</u>	Different
Have 4 sides	
Have 4 corners	
Opposite sides match	
Have all right angles	

What about the shape of each of the corners in these squares and rectangles—are they all the same, or different? . . . The other day you made triangles that had this kind of an angle. We also said that this angle is like the corner of a piece of paper. Who remembers what this is called?

At this point, students should recognize that this is a right angle. Remind students that they have also seen this kind of angle when they worked with the turtle in *LogoPaths*.

Who remembers how you make this kind of an angle when you're moving the turtle on the computer? What do you have to tell the turtle to do in order to "turn the corner"?

If students have had the opportunity to work on the *LogoPaths* activities, they know that they must use the commands **RT 90** (for a right turn) or **LT 90** (for a left turn), in order to make the turtle draw a right angle.

So the turtle turns 90 degrees to make a right angle. This is how mathematicians measure the distance between the two sides of an angle: in degrees, which are like tiny turns. For a right angle, it takes 90 of those turns. So we can also call a right angle a "90-degree angle."

Hearing the term "degrees" used in this context may be confusing to students as they are used to hearing it in reference to temperature. Let them know that in both cases degrees are a unit of measure that can be repeated, just like units of measure they are more familiar with, such as inches or feet.❷

Turn students' attention back to the chart. Once students agree that all of the angles in these figures are the same, and in fact are all right angles, add "Have 4 (or all) right angles" to the chart under "Same," if it is not there already.❸

Math Notes

❷ **Why 90 Degrees?** A right angle is associated with a quarter turn from some pivot point as a circle is being drawn. Because by mathematical convention, a full circle measures 360 degrees, a right angle is one quarter of that ($360 \div 4 = 90$). Most third graders are not ready to conceptualize this idea; however, it is important that they become familiar with the measurement system of angles, starting with 90 degrees as a "landmark."

❸ **Is a Square a Rectangle?** It is likely that students will bring up this question. Since a rectangle is defined as a quadrilateral with four right angles and a square does have this property, a square is a rectangle. However many third graders think of rectangles as having two short and two long sides and so they question how a square could be a rectangle. Students may want to debate this point. You should decide how much time to allow for this discussion if it comes up. Third graders may not be able to come to a conclusion, but they should have the opportunity to express their thinking. They will return to this discussion in Grade 4.

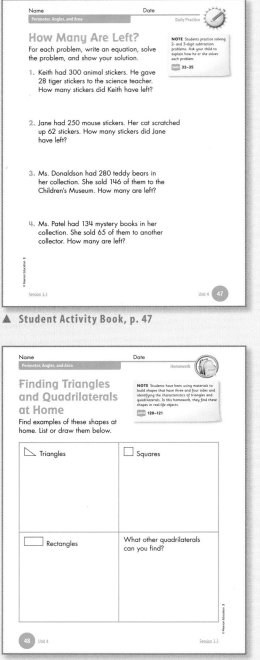

▲ **Student Activity Book, p. 47**

Student Activity Book, p. 48

Now ask students to tell you what is different about the squares and rectangles. Their responses should include that squares have sides that are all the same lengths, while rectangles may only have opposite sides that are the same length. Students may express this in a variety of ways; record several different ways so that students become familiar with this idea using their own words.

Squares and Rectangles	
Same	**Different**
Have 4 sides	Square has all 4
Have 4 corners	sides the same length
Opposite sides match	They're different sizes
Have all right angles	They're different shapes

Post this chart where students can refer back to it as they continue to work on identifying characteristics of shapes and angles.

SESSION FOLLOW-UP

 Daily Practice and Homework

 Daily Practice: For ongoing review, have students complete *Student Activity Book* page 47.

Homework: Students list and/or draw objects that have the shape of triangles, squares, and rectangles on *Student Activity Book* page 48.

 Student Math Handbook: Students and families may use *Student Math Handbook* pages 121, 122–123 for reference and review. See pages 160–164 in the back of this unit.

Angles of Different Sizes

Math Focus Points

◆ Understanding angle size as the degree of turn

◆ Comparing the sizes of angles

Vocabulary

parallelogram

Today's Plan		Materials
① DISCUSSION **Right Angles and Not-Right Angles**	20 MIN · CLASS	• 4″ x 8″ straw rectangle*; moveable angle*
② ACTIVITY **Finding Angles**	40 MIN · PAIRS	• *Student Activity Book,* pp. 49–50 • 2 straws and 1 flexible connector
③ SESSION FOLLOW-UP **Daily Practice**		• *Student Activity Book,* p. 51 • *Student Math Handbook,* pp. 122–123

*See *Materials to Prepare,* p. 101.

Ten-Minute Math

Quick Images: 2-D Show Images 15 and 16 (one at a time) from *Quick Images: 2-D* (T54) and follow the procedure for the basic routine. For each image, students discuss how they drew their figures, including any revisions they made after each viewing.

Ask students:

• How did you remember the parts of the image?

• What did you notice about the relationship of the parts of the image?

• What helped you remember the whole image, so you could draw your design?

Differentiation

❶ **English Language Learners** If possible, meet with English Language Learners ahead of time to preview the questions for this discussion. This will give them the opportunity to practice their responses as you access their understanding and provide language support as needed.

DISCUSSION

Right Angles and Not-Right Angles

20 MIN CLASS

Math Focus Points for Discussion

◆ Understanding angle size as the degree of turn

Begin this session by asking if any students built quadrilaterals in the last session that were not squares or rectangles. Have several students hold up their examples. Choose one or two to talk about briefly, asking:

*How do you know this shape is not a square or rectangle?*❶

Depending on the particular quadrilateral, students may say that the side lengths are not all the same (so it cannot be a square), opposite sides are not the same (so it cannot be a rectangle), or it does not have four right angles (so it cannot be either).

Now show the rectangle you made ahead of time.

Yesterday we noticed that squares and rectangles need to have all right angles. What if I started with this rectangle, and changed it so that its angles are no longer right angles? What would I have to do?

Students might say that you could push it over or squash it down into a shape that is not a rectangle. Have them illustrate with the figure you made.

A student turns a rectangle into a parallelogram by pressing on the top.

Draw the two figures (the rectangle and the now-parallelogram) on the board or overhead.

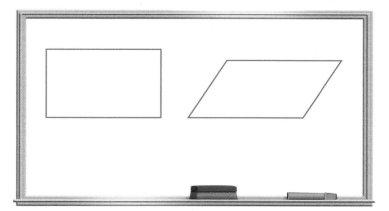

What is the same about the rectangle and this new quadrilateral we just made?

Students should recognize that the side lengths are still the same.

What is different? What changed when we squashed the figure?

Students might say the shape is different or the angles are different.

This figure is a special kind of quadrilateral. Like a rectangle, its sides are *parallel,* which means that the opposite sides look like the sides of railroad tracks. So figures like this are called **parallelograms**. Some parallelograms have right angles and we call them rectangles. Some parallelograms, like this one, do not have right angles.

Point to one of the acute (less than 90 degrees) angles in your parallelogram drawing. You may also hold up the straw-built parallelogram.

Is this angle larger or smaller than a right angle? . . . So if a right angle measures 90 degrees, would the measure of this angle be greater than or less than 90 degrees?

Point to one of the obtuse (greater than 90 degrees) angles.

What about this angle? Is it larger than or smaller than a right angle? . . . Greater than or less than 90 degrees?

Math Note

❶ Acute and Obtuse Angles As with other mathematical vocabulary, you may use these terms yourself when you are describing angles that are less than or greater than 90 degrees, but do not expect third graders to learn and be able to apply these terms accurately. What is more important at this point is for students to be able to use a right angle as a "benchmark" and to recognize the relative size of other angles compared to a right angle: Is it larger or smaller? Students will be expected to learn this vocabulary in later grades, after they have had more experience with measuring angles.

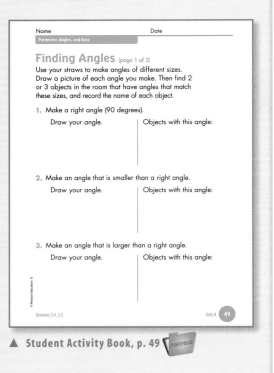

▲ **Student Activity Book, p. 49**

Students may need to measure the obtuse angle against a 90-degree angle to be sure that it is in fact larger. Suggest that someone come up and measure the angle with the corner of a piece of paper.

Hold up the two straws arranged as a right angle. Again point to one of the acute angles (less than 90 degrees) in the parallelogram.

What do I need to do to my straws if I want the straw angle to match this angle?

Students should suggest closing it down or making it smaller. Move the two straws closer together to show how they can match the angle in the drawing.

Ask similar questions to model how the two straws could match an angle greater than 90 degrees (an obtuse angle) using one of the angles in the drawn parallelogram.❶

ACTIVITY

② Finding Angles

40 MIN   PAIRS

Today your job will be to look for angles that are around us. You may find a few or a lot of right angles. You also need to look for angles that are not right angles. They can either be larger or smaller. When you are finding angles today, you can use a two-straw device like this to show various angle sizes.

On *Student Activity Book* pages 49–50, students work with a partner to find angles of various sizes in objects around the room. They use a "moveable" angle made from two straws and a flexible connector to model the sizes of the angles. They use a right angle as a landmark angle. They look for angles that are greater than 90 degrees, less than 90 degrees, much greater than 90 degrees, and much less than 90 degrees. They also write about what an angle is.

Students find objects with angles of various sizes in the classroom.

Students work on this activity for the rest of the session. If they need more time, especially to write what they know about angles, they will have more time during the Math Workshop in the next session. ❷

ONGOING ASSESSMENT: Observing Students at Work

Students find angles of various sizes in the classroom, and compare them to a right angle.

- **Are students able to use the "moveable" angle to locate angles of various sizes?**

- **Do students just choose objects that have one side horizontal or are they able to notice angles that are oriented differently?**

- **Do students notice that the size of the angle is independent of the size of the object (i.e., the corner of the classroom door and the corner of a sheet of paper are both 90-degree angles)?**

- **Do students' lists about what they know about angles include the idea that measuring an angle means examining the amount of turn?**

Math Note

❷ **Finding Angles on Three-Dimensional Objects** Objects in the classroom are three-dimensional. Therefore, as students look for angles, they must pay attention to a two-dimensional surface of a three-dimensional object. For example, the face of the most classroom doors is a two-dimensional rectangle. When students identify an angle on the door as 90 degrees, it is actually the rectangular surface they are working with, not the three-dimensional object (the door) itself.

Name _____ Date _____

Perimeter, Angles, and Area

Finding Angles (page 2 of 2)

Use your straws to make angles of different sizes. Draw a picture of each angle you make. Then find 2 or 3 objects in the room that have angles that match these sizes, and record the name of each object.

4. Make an angle that is much smaller than a right angle.

Draw your angle.	Objects with this angle:

5. Make an angle that is much larger than a right angle.

Draw your angle.	Objects with this angle:

6. List at least three things you know about angles. You may draw pictures if that will help you explain.

50 Unit 4   Sessions 3.4, 3.5

▲ **Student Activity Book, p. 50**

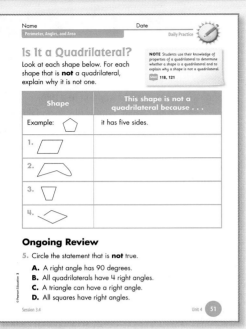

Name _____ **Date** _____

Perimeter, Angles, and Area   Daily Practice

Is It a Quadrilateral?

Look at each shape below. For each shape that is **not** a quadrilateral, explain why it is not one.

NOTE Students use their knowledge of properties of a quadrilateral to determine whether a shape is a quadrilateral and to explain why a shape is not a quadrilateral.
SMH 118, 121

Shape	This shape is not a quadrilateral because . . .
Example:	it has five sides.
1.	
2.	
3.	
4.	

Ongoing Review

5. Circle the statement that is **not** true.

   A. A right angle has 90 degrees.
   B. All quadrilaterals have 4 right angles.
   C. A triangle can have a right angle.
   D. All squares have right angles.

Session 3.4   Unit 4 51

▲ **Student Activity Book, p. 51**

As you observe students working on this activity, ask questions to help them think about what they know about angles:

- Where do you find angles?

- What kind of angles do you know about?

- How big do you think an angle can be? How small?

- How would you tell someone how to make or draw an angle?

DIFFERENTIATION: Supporting the Range of Learners

Intervention If students are having difficulty seeing angles with the "moveable" angle, ask them to form angles with their arms, beginning with a right angle as a landmark, and moving their arms to other positions. Some students might find it useful to move the hands on a clock face. Associating clock hands pointing to 3 o'clock with 90 degrees or a right angle can provide a landmark.

SESSION FOLLOW-UP
3 Daily Practice

Daily Practice: For reinforcement of this unit's content, have students complete *Student Activity Book* page 51.

Student Math Handbook: Students and families may use *Student Math Handbook* pages 122–123 for reference and review. See pages 160–164 in the back of this unit.

Working With Shapes and Angles

Math Focus Points

◆ Understanding angle size as the degree of turn

◆ Comparing the sizes of angles

◆ Identifying the attributes of triangles: three sides, three vertices, and three angles

◆ Identifying the attributes of quadrilaterals: four sides, four vertices, and four angles

Today's Plan		Materials
1 MATH WORKSHOP **Building More Triangles and Quadrilaterals** **1A** Finding Angles **1B** Building More Triangles and Quadrilaterals **1C** *LogoPaths* Activity: *Feed the Turtle* (optional)	40 MIN	**1A** • Materials from Session 3.4, p. 123 **1B** • *Student Activity Book,* pp. 52–53, 37–38 (from Session 3.1; optional), 45–46 (from Session 3.3; optional) • Straw Building Kits **1C** • Computers with *LogoPaths* software installed
2 DISCUSSION **More or Less Than a Right Angle?**	20 MIN CLASS	• *Student Activity Book,* pp. 49–50 • Chart: "Different-Sized Angles"*
3 SESSION FOLLOW-UP **Daily Practice and Homework**		• *Student Activity Book,* pp. 54–55 • *Student Math Handbook,* pp. 120, 121, 122–123

*See *Materials to Prepare,* p. 103.

Ten-Minute Math

Practicing Place Value Write 812 on the board and have students practice saying it to a partner. Make sure all students can read, write, and say this number correctly.

Ask students:

• Find and sketch five or six different ways to make 812 using only sheets of 100, strips of 10, and single stickers (such as 8 sheets, 12 singles or 6 sheets, 21 strips, and 2 singles).

Collect a few examples on the board and ask students how they found their answers.

Did anyone notice a pattern?

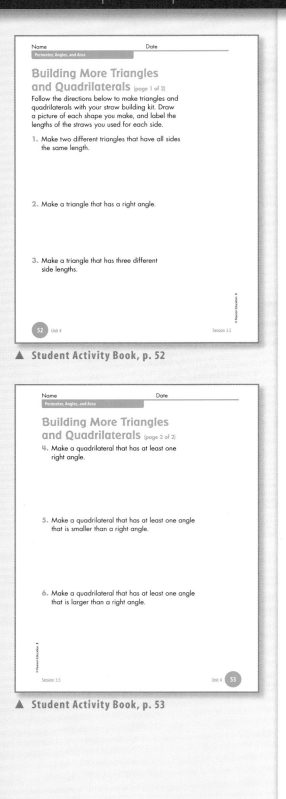

▲ Student Activity Book, p. 52

▲ Student Activity Book, p. 53

MATH WORKSHOP

① Building More Triangles and Quadrilaterals

40 MIN

Students who need more work comparing angles to 90 degrees should spend part of the Math Workshop continuing to find angles in the classroom. Other Math Workshop activities are building a variety of new triangles and quadrilaterals and the optional *LogoPaths* activity, *Feed the Turtle*.

①A Finding Angles

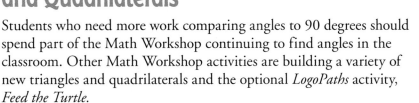
PAIRS **INDIVIDUALS**

For details about this activity, see Session 3.4, pages 126–127.

①B Building More Triangles and Quadrilaterals

PAIRS **INDIVIDUALS**

Students use the straw building kits and follow the directions on *Student Activity Book* pages 52–53 to make a variety of new figures. They may work on this activity either alone or with a partner. If students have not completed either *Student Activity Book* pages 37–38 or *Student Activity Book* pages 45–46, you may decide to have them complete those before going on to the new student sheet.

ONGOING ASSESSMENT: Observing Students at Work

Students build triangles and quadrilaterals using straws for sides and connectors for vertices.

- **Are students able to build triangles and quadrilaterals according to the given constraints?** When they draw these, do they pay attention to the lengths of the sides and try to approximate these? Do they pay attention to angle size, and approximate these as well?

- **Do students choose correct side lengths to make squares?** To make rectangles?

- **Are students able to build quadrilaterals that are not squares or rectangles?**

1C *LogoPaths* Activity: *Feed the Turtle* (optional)

PAIRS   INDIVIDUALS

For details about this activity, see Session 3.3, page 119.

DISCUSSION

② More or Less Than a Right Angle?

20 MIN   CLASS

Math Focus Points for Discussion

◆ Comparing the sizes of angles

Have students bring *Student Activity Book* pages 49–50 to the discussion. In this discussion, students share the objects they found that matched with each of the five categories of angle size (very small, less than 90 degrees, 90 degrees, greater than 90 degrees, and much greater than 90 degrees). Show the "Different-Sized Angles" chart that you prepared.

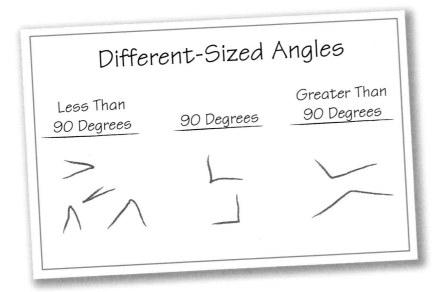

Solicit a few examples of objects that students found to be right angles or 90 degrees, and list them on the chart. Then turn to the category of objects that have angles that are smaller than a right angle. Invite students to point to the objects, show what part of the object they were considering as the angles, and show how they determined it was less than 90 degrees. Have a few students draw the angles on the chart under the heading "Less Than 90 Degrees."

Repeat this process with angles that are greater than 90 degrees. You can record the very large and very small angles as greater than 90 degrees and less than 90 degrees so the chart will have just three categories.

Call the students' attention to two particular examples that will illustrate the possibility that a small figure can have an angle greater than 90 degrees and a large figure can have an angle less than 90 degrees. For example:

[Keisha] showed us an angle that was greater than 90 degrees in this pattern block drawing. [Dwayne] showed us an angle that was less than 90 degrees on the wall poster. How can it be that a small object can have a large angle?

Students might say:

"My angle is large because you have to turn the straws a lot to match it."

"My angle is less than 90 degrees because it is less than a 90-degree turn."

Some students may say that the size of the object does not tell you anything about the size of the angle. Give students time to discuss this, using other examples of angles on different-sized objects to illustrate their point. Some students are likely to be confused about this idea. The fact that the size of an angle is the measure of an amount of turn, rather than the measure of an actual object or figure, is something that students will continue to examine in later grades.

SESSION FOLLOW-UP

Daily Practice and Homework

Daily Practice: For ongoing review, have students complete *Student Activity Book* page 54.

Homework: Students solve problems in which they compare heights and lengths in centimeters on *Student Activity Book* page 55.

Student Math Handbook: Students and families may use *Student Math Handbook* pages 120, 121, 122–123 for reference and review. See pages 160–164 in the back of this unit.

Name _____ Date _____
Perimeter, Angles, and Area   Daily Practice

Make $1.00, Make $2.00

NOTE Students practice finding combinations of amounts that add to a given total.

1. Fill in the blanks to make combinations of four amounts that add up to $1.00.

Example:
$0.25 + 0.25 + 0.40 + 0.10 = $1.00
____ + 0.15 + ____ + ____ = $1.00
____ + ____ + 0.10 + ____ = $1.00
____ + 0.30 + ____ + ____ = $1.00

2. Now fill in the blanks to make combinations of four amounts that add up to $2.00.
____ + 0.35 + ____ + ____ = $2.00
____ + ____ + 0.60 + ____ = $2.00
____ + ____ + ____ + 0.95 = $2.00

54 Unit 4   Session 3.5

▲ Student Activity Book, p. 54

Name _____ Date _____
Perimeter, Angles, and Area   Homework

How Much Taller?
How Much Longer?

NOTE Students compare heights and lengths in centimeters.

For each problem, write an equation, solve the problem, and show your solution. You may use number lines or drawings to help you explain your thinking.

1. Mr. Vega is 185 centimeters tall. Oscar is 129 centimeters tall. How much taller is Mr. Vega than Oscar?

2. An NBA basketball player is 216 centimeters tall. How much taller is the basketball player than Mr. Vega?

3. The Burmese python at the Midtown Zoo is 330 centimeters long. The boa constrictor is 217 centimeters long. How much longer is the Burmese python?

Session 3.5   Unit 4   55

▲ Student Activity Book, p. 55

End-of-Unit Assessment

Math Focus Points

◆ Identifying the attributes of triangles: three sides, three vertices, and three angles

◆ Finding area by counting or calculating whole and partial square units

◆ Identifying a right angle as having a measure of 90 degrees

◆ Comparing the sizes of angles

Today's Plan		Materials
① ASSESSMENT ACTIVITY **End-of-Unit Assessment**	✔ 🕐 👤 60 MIN INDIVIDUALS	• M22–M24*
② SESSION FOLLOW-UP **Daily Practice**		• *Student Activity Book*, p. 57 • *Student Math Handbook*, pp. 115, 120, 121, 122–123

*See *Materials to Prepare*, p. 103.

Ten-Minute Math

Practicing Place Value Say "seven hundred forty-two" and ask students to write the number. Make sure all students can read, write, and say this number correctly. Ask students to solve these problems mentally, if possible:

• What is 742 − 40? 742 − 20? 742 + 40? 742 − 400? 742 − 200? 742 + 400?

Write each answer on the board. Have students compare each sum or difference with 742. Ask students the following questions:

• Which places have the same digits? Which do not? Why?

If time remains, pose additional similar problems using these numbers: 668 and 713.

1

ASSESSMENT ACTIVITY
End-of-Unit Assessment

60 MIN INDIVIDUALS

On End-of-Unit Assessment (M22–M24), students work individually to solve three problems designed to assess three of the unit's benchmarks. ❶

In Problem 1, which addresses Benchmark 2: identify and find the area of given figures by counting whole and partial square units, students find the area of an irregular polygon. For Problem 2, students identify shapes that are triangles and explain their choices. This problem addresses Benchmark 3: identify triangles as three-sided closed figures with three vertices and three angles. In Problem 3, which addresses Benchmark 4: identify right angles, and recognize whether an angle is larger or smaller than a right angle, students identify angles as equal to, less than, or greater than 90°.

Students who finish this assessment before the end of the math session may work on the computer *LogoPaths* activities or return to any unfinished Math Workshop activities.

ONGOING ASSESSMENT: Observing Students at Work

Students find area in square units, use attributes to identify triangles, and compare angles to 90-degree angles. ❷

- **Are students able to find area in square units?** Does their work show their strategy for doing so?

- **Do students recognize that shapes must be closed figures with three sides, three vertices, and three angles, in order to be triangles?**

- **Do they recognize that in order to be a triangle a shape cannot have any curved sides?**

- **Do students recognize that triangles can be oriented in many ways?**

- **Are students able to identify the angles that are 90 degrees?**

- **Do they accurately identify the angles that are greater than or less than 90 degrees?**

Professional Development

❶ **Teacher Note:** End-of-Unit Assessment, p. 149

Teaching Note

❷ **End-of-Unit Assessment:** Students find the area of an irregular shape, use attributes to distinguish triangles from non-triangles, identify 90-degree angles, and compare other angles to 90 degrees. This assessment addresses Benchmarks 2, 3, and 4.

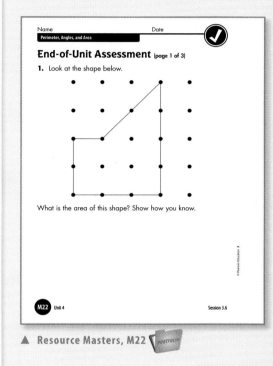

▲ **Resource Masters, M22**

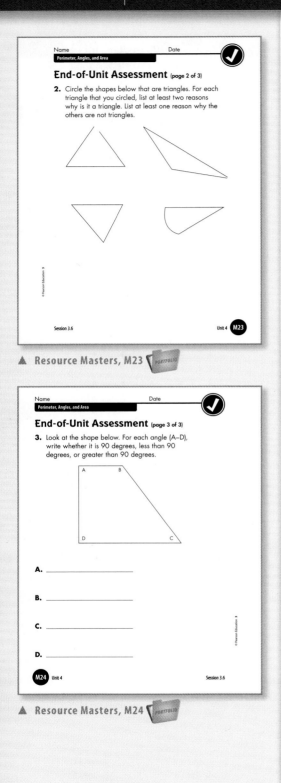

▲ Resource Masters, M23

▲ Resource Masters, M24

2 **SESSION FOLLOW-UP**

Daily Practice

 Daily Practice: For enrichment, have students complete *Student Activity Book* page 57.

Student Math Handbook: Students and families may use *Student Math Handbook* pages 115, 120, 121, 122–123 for reference and review. See pages 160–164 in the back of this unit.

How Big Is Our Classroom?

NOTE Students identify and accurately measure the perimeter of a shape using U.S. Standard and metric units.

SMH 110–111, 112

1. Estimate how many yardstick lengths it will take to measure the perimeter of your classroom.

2. Multiply the number of yardsticks by 3 to get an accurate estimate of the perimeter in feet.

3. Measure the perimeter of the room as best you can. You may want to have one person measure with the yardstick and the other person keep a tally of how many yardstick lengths you use.

4. After you have measured the actual perimeter of your classroom, skip count or multiply by 3 to get the measurement in feet (instead of yards).

Answer the following questions:

1. How many yardstick lengths do you think it will take to find the perimeter of your classroom? _____

2. What do you estimate the perimeter of your classroom to be in feet? _____

3. How many yardstick lengths did it actually take to measure the perimeter of your classroom? _____

4. What is the perimeter of your classroom in feet? _____

5. Do you think you made an accurate estimate of the classroom's perimeter? Explain why or why not. _____

Session 3.6   Unit 4 **57**

▲ Student Activity Book, p. 57

Professional Development

UNIT 4

Perimeter, Angles, and Area

In Part 6 of *Implementing Investigations in Grade 3,* you will find a set of Teacher Notes that addresses topics and issues applicable to the curriculum as a whole rather than to specific curriculum units. They include the following:

Computational Fluency and Place Value

Computational Algorithms and Methods

Representations and Contexts for Mathematical Work

Foundations of Algebra in the Elementary Grades

Discussing Mathematical Ideas

Racial and Linguistic Diversity in the Classroom:
   What Does Equity Mean in Today's Math Classroom?

Metric and U.S. Standard Units of Measure

Only the United States and two other countries are not officially metric. In many countries, people are unfamiliar with the U.S. (or English) standard units that we use. They buy food by the kilogram and drinks by the liter. They drive kilometers per hour in cars powered with gas bought by the liter. They know their height in centimeters, their weight in kilograms, and the temperature in Celsius.

Most countries use the metric system, and the increasingly global marketplace has led experts to predict that the United States will soon convert. It is important for students to become familiar with metric measurement, as well as work with U.S. standard measures including pounds, feet, and miles.

One useful aspect of the metric system is that it is based on powers of 10. This simplifies calculations and conversions. Prefixes are used across measurement types to denote the magnitude, or power of 10, of the measure in question. The most common of these are *kilo-*, *centi-*, and *milli-*. *Kilo-* means 1,000, therefore 1,000 meters is a *kilometer*. *Centi-* means one-hundredth, therefore one-hundredth of a meter is a *centimeter*. *Milli-* means one-thousandth; a *millimeter* is one-thousandth of a meter. Other metric prefixes, such as *deca-*, *deci-*, and *hecta-*, are less commonly used.

Adults who are accustomed to U.S. standard measure may use them as benchmarks to get a sense of metric units. For example, you probably know that a meter is a little longer than a yard and that a kilometer is a little longer than half a mile.

In this unit, students learn about linear metric measures through their own experiences as they compare them to objects. Thus, they might learn:

A millimeter is about the thickness of a dime or a paper clip wire.

A centimeter is about the width of a paper clip.

A meter is about the length from the tip of your fingers to your opposite shoulder.

The height of a tall man is about 200 centimeters.

Students become familiar with metric measurements.

Making Careful Measurements

At the beginning of the year, most third graders have had limited experience taking measurements. Those who have done sewing or woodworking are more likely to be able to measure accurately, and may also have a better sense of when a measurement is "about right" and when it needs to be checked. To measure accurately, students need both mechanical skills and conceptual understandings. Techniques that are important for careful measuring include the following:

- Lining up the measurement tool exactly at zero when beginning a new measurement, and reading the calibrations on the measurement tool correctly

- Working either in meters and centimeters or feet and inches—but not a mixture of metric and standard systems

- Positioning the measuring tool against the object being measured

- Measuring from the same end of the measurement tool with each repeated use when measuring a large distance

- Accurately approximating the final portion of the measurement

- Keeping track of partial measurements and calculating the total measurement

Important concepts to understand include the following:

- Knowing *why* these measurement techniques are important—for example, why metric and standard units should not be combined in measurements

- Recognizing when precise measurement is needed and when it is not

- Knowing how to determine if a measurement is reasonable or if it is necessary to check it

As students work on measurement activities, circulate through the class to observe. This way, you can help them learn the skill of measuring while they are actually doing it. You can also discuss with students the reasonableness of their measurements, help them explore possible sources of measurement error, and encourage them to check and revise measurements as needed.

Introducing and Managing the *LogoPaths* Software

LogoPaths software is provided as a component of the *Investigations* curriculum.

While the use of this software is optional, it is highly recommended if you have computers available. In this unit, *LogoPaths* games and activities are introduced in each Investigation and then integrated into the Math Workshop activities. The software activities extend and deepen the mathematical ideas that are emphasized in this unit, and in some cases the software activities allow students to work with geometric figures and angles in ways that they are not able to in the off-computer activities.

In this unit, activities with the *LogoPaths* software are suggested throughout each Investigation. How you introduce and incorporate *LogoPaths* activities into your curriculum depends on the number of computers and computer technology that you have available. First, you will need to consider how you will introduce your students to the *LogoPaths* software. Then, you will need to consider how students will have access to the software. You may want to introduce each new software activity to the whole class if you have access to a large screen projection setup. If you have access to a computer lab, consider introducing each new activity to the whole class in this environment. In this unit the activities are included as Math Workshop activities, so once students are introduced to an activity, they can then access the activity during Math Workshop. If your school has a computer teacher, consider collaborating with that teacher to have students work on these activities during some of their scheduled time in the computer lab.

Regardless of the number of computers you have, students generally benefit from working on these activities in pairs. This not only maximizes computer resources, but also encourages students to consult, monitor, and teach each other. Generally, more than two students find it difficult to share one computer. You may need to monitor computer use closely to ensure that all students get sufficient computer time. Each pair should spend at least 15–20 minutes at the computer for each activity.

Options for Introducing the *LogoPaths* Software

Computer Lab If you have a computer laboratory with one computer for each pair of students, all of your students can be introduced to and become familiar with the computer activities at the same time. In this situation, you will not need to devote time during math class to introduce students to the new software activity. Students will access the activity during Math Workshop.

Large Screen Monitor or Projection Screen If you have access to either of these devices, you can introduce the software activities to the whole class during the math session immediately before Math Workshop or at another time of the day.

Small Groups of Students You can introduce the software activities to small groups of students either before or during Math Workshop. These students can then be paired with other students and become "teachers" of the software.

Managing the Computer Environment

Math Workshop Students should have access to the *LogoPaths* software consistently throughout the unit. If you have daily access to a computer lab, you might choose to add this experience into your day in addition to your regular math class. A more typical computer situation is that classrooms have a small number of computers. While three to five computers is ideal, students can have a successful computer experience with only one to two computers. In the case of fewer computers, you will need to incorporate additional computer time for students throughout the day. If you have computers available in your classroom, pairs of students can cycle through the computer activities, just as they cycle through the other Math Workshop activities.

Using *LogoPaths* All Year This is the only unit in the Grade 3 sequence that explicitly suggests computer activities to go with the specific sessions of the unit. However, along with the suggested activities in units prior to this one, suggestions and Teacher Resources are included in later units for activities that students can continue for the remainder of the school year. Continued experience with *LogoPaths* allows them to become increasingly fluent in the mechanics of the software itself and able to better focus on the mathematical ideas of the games and activities. Students should continue to explore the games that develop understanding of paths and turning angles and the *Free Explore* activities that focus on the properties of 2-D shapes, including their angles. Students will build on their knowledge and experiences with the *LogoPaths* software in Grades 4 and 5.

Introducing the *LogoPaths* Activities

In your first introduction of the ***Get the Toys*** game, show students the following:

- How to open *LogoPaths* by double-clicking on the icon

- How to open *Get the Toys* by clicking on it once

- How to select the level they wish to play

- How to enter forward and backward commands in multiples of 10 steps (e.g., **FD** 50 **BK** 100)

- How to enter commands to turn right or left 90° (**RT** 90 **LT** 90)

- How to use the **Label Lengths** and **Label Turns** tools

In your first introduction of the ***Missing Measures*** and the ***200 (400, 500) Steps*** activities, show students the following:

- How to open *Free Explore* by clicking on it once

- How to enter forward and back commands of any number (e.g., **FD** 82 **BK** 125). (Note that move and turn inputs must be between −999 and 999.)

- How to use the **HT** (hide turtle) and **ST** (show turtle) commands

- How to use the **Teach** tool to make a procedure out of a set of commands in the Command Center. You will be asked to give it a name, and the commands will be moved to the Teach window in the proper format for a procedure.

In your first introduction of the ***Feed the Turtle*** game, show students the following:

- How to open *Feed the Turtle* by clicking on it once

- How to select the level they wish to play

- How to enter forward and back commands of any number (e.g., **FD** 82 **BK** 125)

- How to enter commands to turn right or left in multiples of 30° (e.g., **RT** 30 **RT** 120 **LT** 60 **LT** 180)

- How to use the **Turtle Turner** and the **Ruler** tools.

You can introduce more of the tools available in *LogoPaths* as students indicate interest and the need to use them.

- Students can use the penup (**PU**) and pendown (**PD**) commands to tell the turtle whether or not to draw as it moves. Type **PU** in the Command Center to move without drawing. Type **PD** for the turtle to draw as it moves.

- The repeat command tells the turtle to repeat a set of commands a specified number of times. The first input is the number of times to repeat, and the second is a list of commands enclosed in square brackets. For example, to repeat a forward move and a right turn three times, students might type repeat 3 [**FD** 100 **RT** 90].

- You can hide the turtle by typing "**HT**". Type "**ST**" in the Command Center to see the turtle again.

- Students can change the color, shape, and size of the turtle and the line it draws using the Turtle Features panel ⬚. Other features of how the turtle works (e.g., its speed) can be changed in the Preferences panel ⬚.

Further information about commands, tools, and buttons can be found in the online Help ⬚.

It is likely that many students will discover other tools and their uses on their own as they spend more time working with the software. Encourage them to share their discoveries with each other.

Saving Student Work

If you want to discuss students' work later, have them either print it (if your computers are connected to a printer) or save their work on disks. For information about printing or saving to a disk, refer to the *Software Support Reference Guide* contained on the CD in your curriculum guide package.

About the Mathematics in the *LogoPaths* Software

The *LogoPaths* software provides an environment in which students can explore geometry, patterns, logical thinking, and more. The essential metaphor in Logo is "playing turtle"—taking the perspective of the turtle (the drawing cursor) to move and turn to make shapes and designs. This is a very natural view of geometry for students because it matches how individuals explore the world—through questions such as "How much further do I need to move?" and "Which way should I turn to get to a particular place?"

When they use *LogoPaths,* students explore a number of geometric and other mathematical ideas. This includes explicit investigation of length and perimeter and the equality of lengths of opposite sides in a parallelogram. It also includes exploration of the sizes of angles and the relationship between the turning (or exterior) angle and the interior angle of polygons. *LogoPaths* is another context in which students come to see a variety of representations of numerical ideas—bigger or smaller means a different thing with respect to length, angle, number of sides, etc.

Using the *LogoPaths* software in Grades 3 through 5 also allows students to explore many kinds of patterns and relationships. For example, they discover that the first two sides of a rectangle always have half the total perimeter; that consecutive sides of a parallelogram have turning angles that total 180°; that a polygon with only 90 degree turns always has an even number of sides; and that the turning (exterior) angles in a polygon total 360 degrees (which means that the turning angle in a regular polygon is always 360 divided by the number of sides). You can encourage students to look for a wide variety of patterns and see whether they can explain when they are true and why. Creating procedures with variable inputs is another way of focusing on regularities and patterns; such procedures define a whole class of shapes with the same structure but with different sizes, angles, etc.

LogoPaths offers students a chance to see a variety of inverse operations—that is, pairs of commands that undo one another's effects. For example, moving forward and then back the same amount leaves the turtle in the same place. Other inverse operations include right and left, penup and pendown, and hide turtle and show turtle. Students can also explore arithmetic inverses with addition and subtraction, multiplication and division, or positive and negative numbers. *LogoPaths* allows students to pair the concept of an inverse with a visual component.

Students also learn careful logical thinking by working with *LogoPaths*. Because the turtle only does exactly what students tell it to do, students learn to be precise in their instructions. If the turtle does something unexpected, students learn to break down the instructions step by step; by "playing turtle" to figure out just how their instructions led to this unexpected behavior, students can deduce how to change that behavior. Some of *LogoPaths*' debugging tools (e.g., the Stop tool, the Step tool, and highlighting of steps, even through procedures in the Teach window) can help in this process. (The *Software Support Reference Guide* and the Help text provide more information about these tools.) By making procedures that can be used by other procedures, students also break down complex ideas and projects into smaller, more manageable chunks. For example, a procedure to make a house might move the turtle to the right positions and then use a square procedure for windows, a rectangle procedure for the door, and a triangle procedure for the roof. These sorts of logical and analytical problem-solving approaches are important to mathematical thinking.

What's an -Omino?

A *domino,* as you know, is the shape formed by putting two squares together, with full edges touching. There is only one shape you can make with two squares:

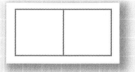

Adding a third square makes a *triomino.* A triomino has two possible arrangements:

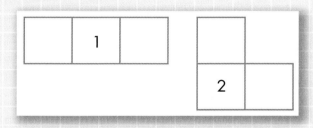

Triominoes A, B, and C may look like other possible arrangements, but they are the same shape as Triominoes 1 or 2.

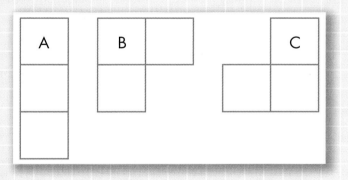

That is, these shapes can move through space, with a *flip* (reflection) or a *turn* (rotation), and then a slide, to exactly match Triomino 1 or 2.

To see firsthand how this works, make Triomino B out of interlocking cubes. Watch how you move it to make it look exactly like Triomino 2. Is there more than one series of motions that will work? Triomino 2 and Triomino B are congruent—the same size and shape. What about the other triominoes?

You should have discovered that Triomino B becomes Triomino 2 with a flip and a slide, Triomino A becomes Triomino 1 with a turn and a slide, and Triomino C becomes Triomino 2 with a 90-degree turn and a slide.

Now use interlocking cubes and try making the set of tetrominoes—all the possible arrangements of four squares with full sides touching. Remember, if you can move a tetromino through a series of slides, flips, and turns so that it exactly matches another tetromino, it is not a different arrangement. How do you know when you have found all of the combinations? Can you convince yourself that there cannot possibly be any other tetrominoes?

Understanding the Area of Triangles

In this unit, students learn about measuring area as "covering a flat space with square units." Finding the area of triangles is studied in this unit by looking at each triangle in relationship to a related rectangle. For example, it is easy to see that the smaller of the two triangles on the Square and Triangle Cut-Outs is half a square unit.

When students are comfortable with the unit square as one square unit and the small triangle as a half of a unit, spend time talking about the one-unit triangle.

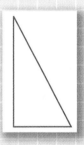

Students can use their Tetromino Puzzle to help them think about how the triangle is related to one square unit. Here are two ways to think about it: First, you can think of this shape as half of a 2-unit rectangle. Since the rectangle is two square units and the triangle is half of the whole shape, you can conclude that the triangle is half of two—or one square unit:

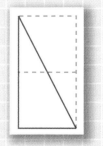

Students may express this by saying something like, "Two of them together makes two squares, so each of them must be one square unit."

Another way to see that this triangle has an area of one square unit is to cut the triangle into two pieces and rearrange the pieces to make a unit square.

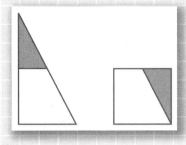

Some students will immediately "see" this relationship as they look at the unit triangle drawn on top of the 2-unit rectangle.

Initially it is fine if some of your students are only comfortable with the square and half-unit triangle as a measure of area. If your students do use the larger one-unit triangle to make new shapes later on, make sure that they can prove the area of the shapes.

For example, suppose they make the shape below (at left).

Students might say:

"See, if you cut off this piece (piece 1) and turned it around and put it over on the other side, like this (see the second figure), it would cover four squares."

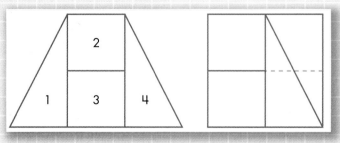

If students say only "Because this triangle is 1," they may just be repeating what they have heard from you or other students. Be sure they can explain why the area is 1 by one of the methods discussed in this note or by some other convincing method of their own.

Assessment: Make a Shape

Benchmark addressed:

Benchmark 2: Identify and find the area of given figures by counting whole and partial square units.

In order to meet the benchmark, students' work should show that they can:

- Accurately create a shape composed of squares and triangles with an area of 5, 6, or 7 square units;

- Justify their solution in writing.

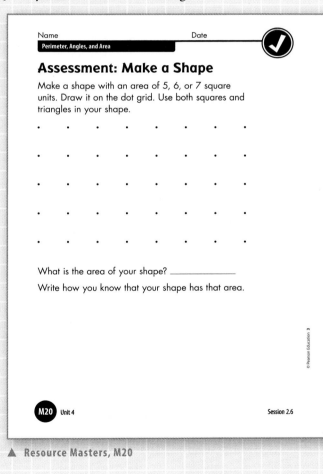

▲ Resource Masters, M20

Meeting the Benchmark

These students are able to draw a shape and clearly show its area. They understand how much area the half unit and unit triangles cover and are able to explain how they calculated the area. Kenji and Elena, for example, are both students who meet the benchmark.

Kenji: I know that there are five because two triangles make one square exactly, and one square makes one. My design has six triangles, and six triangles make three, and two squares make two, and three plus two makes five square units.

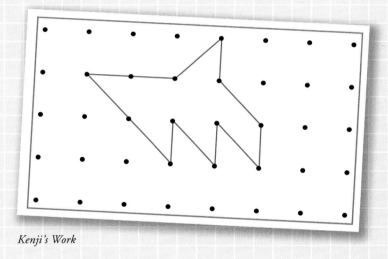

Kenji's Work

Elena: There are four of the little triangles. That's four halves, so that makes two. Then there's two of the big triangles. If you put them together like I did they cover two squares, so that's two more. That's four so far. Then there's two regular squares. So two more makes six squares.

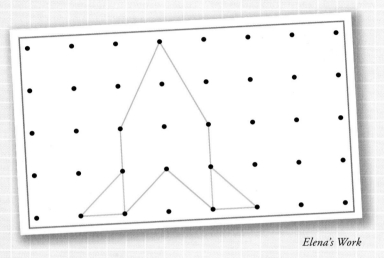

Elena's Work

Both Kenji and Elena demonstrate their knowledge of the relationships between triangles and squares and explain how to combine the pieces to find the area of their shapes. Elena has set herself a somewhat harder task by including the unit triangle in her shape.

Partially Meeting the Benchmark

These students may accurately draw shapes with five, six, or seven square units, but fail to show or explain fully how they calculated the area of those shapes. Philip and Gina are examples of students who partially meet the benchmark.

Philip: I know that my shape has six square units because it has two squares and eight triangles and when you add them together you get six square units.

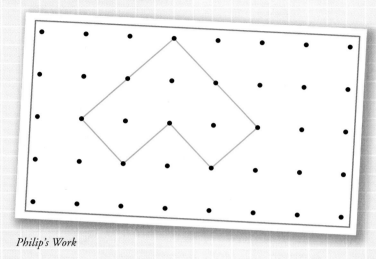

Philip's Work

Gina: I counted them in halves and in wholes. The triangles are the halves and the wholes are the squares.

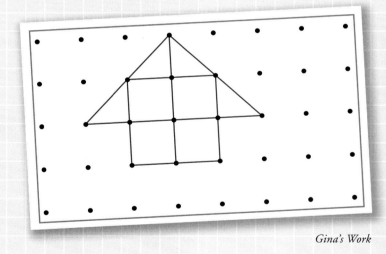

Gina's Work

Philip and Gina may have a clear understanding of how to use the squares and triangles to measure the area of their shapes, but they have difficulty writing down their explanations. Try questioning students like Philip and Gina further to determine their ability to explain why a triangle is equal to half a square unit.

Not Meeting the Benchmark

These students do not successfully draw shapes with five, six, or seven square units or are unable to write adequate explanations of how they calculated the area. Benjamin and Kathryn are examples of students who do not meet the benchmark.

Benjamin does create a shape with five square units, but his writing does not state that, and he fails to explain what he knows about how much area is covered by the square and triangular units in his design.

Benjamin: There are three squares and four triangles.

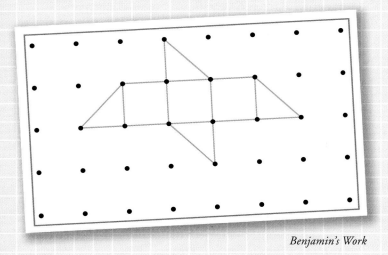

Benjamin's Work

Ask students like Benjamin questions to determine whether or not they understand area as a covering of flat space. For example:

You wrote that there are three squares and four triangles in your design. What does that tell you about how much space your design covers? Can you explain how you know that?

In addition to her inadequate explanation, Kathryn does not successfully draw a shape with five, six, or seven square units. (Her shape has $6\frac{1}{2}$ square units.)

Kathryn: Because it's different and I like it.

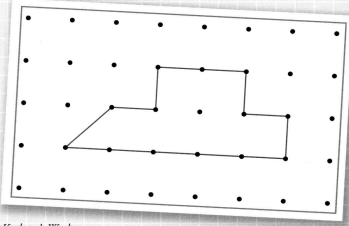

Kathryn's Work

Kathryn's writing could be a sign that she misunderstood what was meant when she was asked to write about her mathematical thinking. She may be answering a question like, "What do you think of this problem?" Further conversation with students like Kathryn is needed to determine what they understand about the problem itself. For example:

What did this problem ask you to do? Tell me about your shape. How many squares are in your shape? How many triangles? . . . Can you tell me how many square units are in your shape altogether? How do you know?

Teacher Note

Beyond Vocabulary

In this unit, students will be introduced to vocabulary words they may not yet know as they work in groups and as a class to describe kinds and characteristics of triangles, quadrilaterals, and angles. Initially, as students construct polygons and angles from the straw building kits and as you and the students discuss their results, you will hear them talk about the shapes in their own words. For example, a "pointy angle" may mean an acute angle (less than 90 degrees), and a "wide angle" may be an obtuse one (greater than 90 degrees). The activities in this investigation, however, will motivate students to use more precise language. As students work to make themselves clear, you will hear some unusual, but accurate, descriptions. For example, one third grader described angles this way:

"An angle is two lines attached by the ends. They're either pulling away from each other or pushing to get closer. The shape they make while doing that is the angle."

Although, mathematically, the "lines" in the student's description are actually rays (meaning that they continue on indefinitely), the student does understand that an angle is formed by two sides and a vertex. She also has a sense of the motion of turning that defines the size of the angle, which she visualizes as "pulling away" or "pushing closer." At this point, having such a visual image will serve her far better than being given a more mathematically correct definition of "angle." For all students, it is important to try to achieve a balance between using the most accurate words and agreeing on classroom vocabulary that makes the most sense to students.

Students will learn the mathematical terms as they hear them in context. Use the correct terms yourself and informally explain to students what they mean. As students hear you and others use the terms, they will adopt the ones that make sense to them. However, this process will take time; do not expect students to use terms as soon as they hear them. The activities in this investigation provide repeated experience with the same terms and concepts, so students will have a number of opportunities to pick up new vocabulary. Be aware that some students will adopt terms easily, while others will need more time and exposure.

Avoid the temptation to stop and teach a lesson specifically on vocabulary or to test students on vocabulary words. What's more important is that students develop accurate concepts for shapes for which they already have names. Many third-graders (and even older students) have very limited ideas about common shapes. For example, they may call a rectangle a square, or may believe that a triangle must have symmetry (must have two equal sides) and must not be tilted on the page. Help students build concepts without giving them definitions. Allow them to try out their ideas in class discussions, but expect them to make themselves clear and to justify their conjectures.

End-of-Unit Assessment

Problem 1

Benchmark addressed:

Benchmark 2: Identify and find the area of given figures by counting whole and partial square units.

In order to meet the benchmark, students' work should show that they can:

- Accurately determine the area in square units of the given figure;

- Justify their solution in writing and/or numerically.

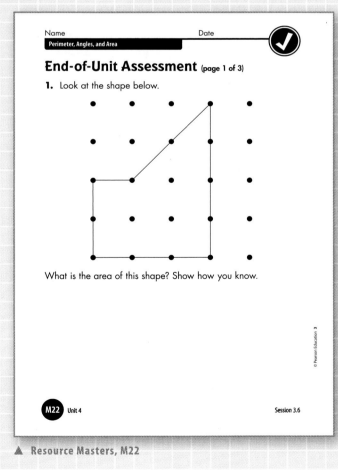

Meeting the Benchmark

These students accurately determine the area of the given figure (eight square units). They understand that area means the space inside the shape. They understand how much area the half-unit triangles cover and are able to explain how they calculated the area of the whole figure.

Arthur, for example, drew lines to show the seven squares and two triangles.

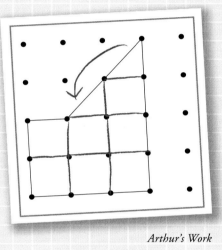

Arthur's Work

He wrote:

"8 square units. If you take both of the triangles and put them together it will make a square unit, and then just count the rest of the squares. There are 7, and $7 + 1 = 8$."

Deondra drew lines and also numbered the full squares 1–7. She drew an arc between the two triangles and labeled the arc with an 8.

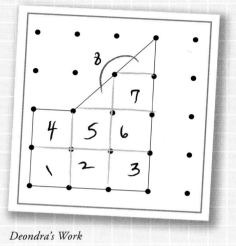

Deondra's Work

She wrote:

"The area of this shape is 8 square units. I found out by filling in the lines to make square units. There were 7 full squares. Then I did half and half is 8 square units."

Bridget drew no lines, but wrote:

8 square units   7 full squares

2 triangles = 1 full square

7 + 1 = 8 square units

Partially Meeting the Benchmark

Some students may number the whole and half square units within the shape, but fail to record the total area. Beatriz, for example, labeled the squares 1–7 and each triangle $\frac{1}{2}$, but never added the two halves to the 7. Ask students like Beatriz if they can tell you the total area of the shape.

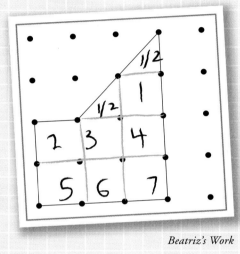

Beatriz's Work

Other students may demonstrate understanding of the squares as one square unit and the triangles as $\frac{1}{2}$ square unit, but then miscount, resulting in an incorrect total area. Murphy, for example, labeled each whole unit within the shape and one of the half-unit triangles. Therefore, when he calculated the area, he came up with a total of $7\frac{1}{2}$ square units.

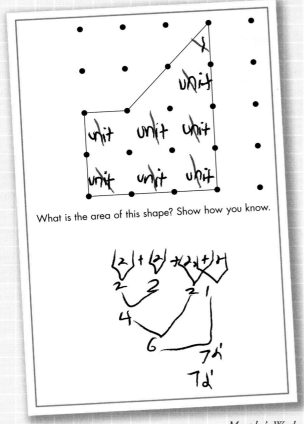

Murphy's Work

Students like Nicholas do show understanding of whole and half units and may therefore have misunderstood the task. Ask questions to determine what they understand. For example:

I see that you drew lines to show the squares and triangles in the shape. How many whole units do you see? How many half units? What does that tell you about the area of the shape?

Other students may not include the area of the triangles in their calculations. Kim, for example, recorded the area as 7. She wrote:

"I know because I counted the little square units and that's how I got my answer."

Ask students like Kim to consider if they have accounted for the entire area of the shape. For example:

I see that you've counted all of the squares. Is there any space left inside the shape that you didn't count? How can you figure out how many square units that space equals?

Other students may not understand the concept of area as covering space. Edwin, for example, recorded 13 as his answer. He wrote:

"It's 13 because it has 13 dots and 5 sides."

Edwin seems to have (incorrectly) counted the dots around the perimeter of the figure and may be confusing perimeter with area. Ask students like Edwin questions to determine what they understand.

Can you use your hand to show me the area of this shape? Can you show me the perimeter?

Students like Edwin need more experience finding the area of rectangular arrays and relating the area of the half-unit triangles to the unit squares.

Students like Murphy may be able to self-correct when questioned about their work. In addition, they may benefit from drawing lines within the figure (if they have not already done so) to see more clearly the whole and half square units.

Not Meeting the Benchmark

These students do not accurately determine the area of the shape. Their work may be incomplete. Nicholas, for example, drew lines to show the whole and half squares but failed to include the area of the shape in his work. He wrote:

"I drew squares inside the shape. If you take the two halves of squares and put them together you get a box."

Problem 2

Benchmark addressed:

Benchmark 3: Identify triangles as three-sided closed figures with three vertices and three angles.

In order to meet the benchmark, students' work should show that they can:

- Accurately identify the triangles from the group of four figures;

- Correctly write at least two attributes that make each of the figures they chose a triangle;

- Correctly write at least one reason why the figures they did **not** choose are not triangles.

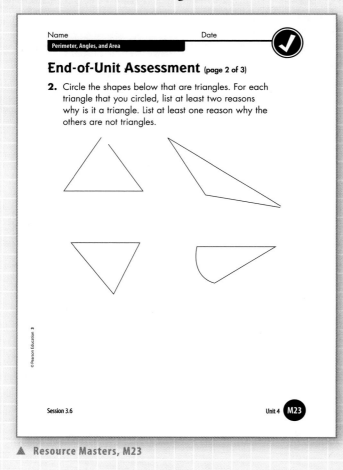

▲ **Resource Masters, M23**

Meeting the Benchmark

These students identify the figures that are triangles and write at least two correct attributes that determine this classification. They also write at least one reason why the other figures are not triangles. Keisha, for example, circled the triangles and wrote:

"I thought these two were triangles because they both have three straight lines and three angles and three vertices. The first shape is not connected so it's not a triangle. The other one has a curved side. Triangles don't have curved sides."

Partially Meeting the Benchmark

These students may identify the figures that are triangles, but for each triangle write fewer than two correct attributes that determine this classification. Dwayne, for example, wrote the following:

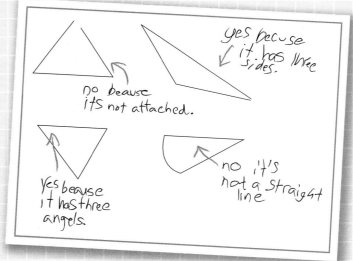

Dwayne's Work

Other students may identify the triangles, write two correct attributes for each triangle, but fail to list reasons the other figures are not triangles. It is possible that students like Dwayne and those who failed to write explanations for the non-triangular figures may have misread the directions and could self-correct if asked to look at the task again. Question these students to determine where their confusion lies.

Not Meeting the Benchmark

Some students in this group fail to identify one or both of the figures that are triangles. Others identify the triangles but fail to write any attributes that determine their classification or write an attribute true of polygons in general, but not particular to triangles. Adam, for example, circled the correct figures, but wrote:

"They are triangles because they have straight lines."

Ask these students what they remember about the definition of triangles you developed as a class and how they can use that definition to help them find the figures in Problem 3 that are triangles.

Problem 3

Benchmark addressed:

Benchmark 4: Identify right angles, and recognize whether an angle is larger or smaller than a right angle.

In order to meet the benchmark, students' work should show that they can:

- Accurately identify the right angles in the figure (Angles A and D);

- Accurately identify the angle that is greater than 90 degrees (Angle B) and the angle that is less than 90 degrees (Angle C).

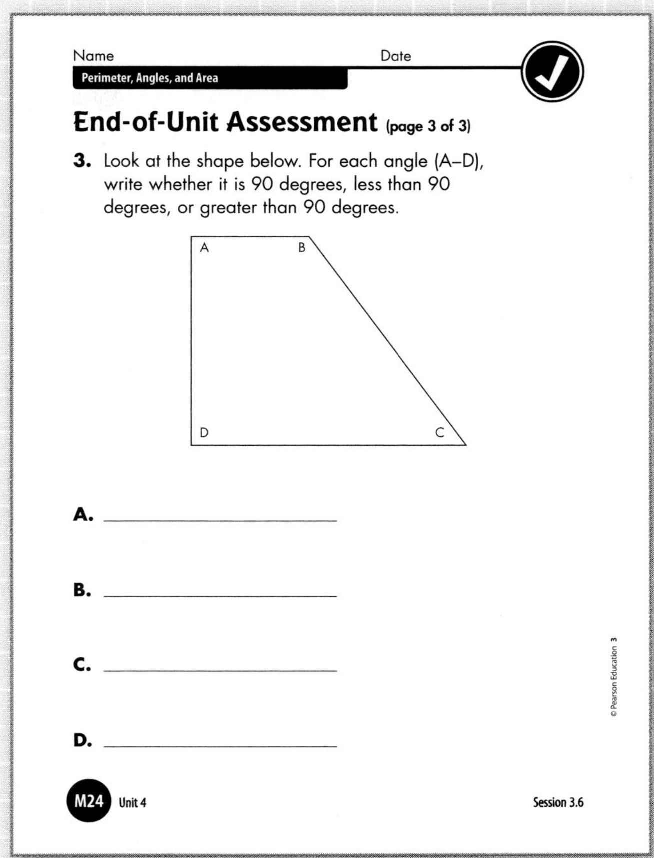

Name _____ Date _____

Perimeter, Angles, and Area

End-of-Unit Assessment (page 3 of 3)

3. Look at the shape below. For each angle (A–D), write whether it is 90 degrees, less than 90 degrees, or greater than 90 degrees.

A. _____

B. _____

C. _____

D. _____

M24   Unit 4   Session 3.6

© Pearson Education 3

▲ Resource Masters, M24

Meeting the Benchmark

These students correctly identify Angles A and D as right angles, Angle B as greater than 90 degrees, and Angle C as less than 90 degrees.

Partially Meeting the Benchmark

These students correctly identify Angles A and D as right angles and recognize that angles B and C are not 90 degrees. They may, however, make errors in determining which angle is greater and which is less than 90 degrees. Check with these students to find out where their confusion lies. It is possible that for some, this is a vocabulary issue.

Can you show me a 90-degree angle with your arm? Where is the angle? . . . Now can you show me an angle that is greater than 90 degrees? Do you know what I mean by greater than? . . . What about one that is less than 90 degrees?

Other students may correctly identify Angle C as less than 90 degrees but may fail to correctly identify Angle B as greater than 90 degrees. This could be the result of Angle B's "upside down" orientation. Check to see if this is the problem by turning the figure upside down and asking the students what they notice about the size of the angle.

Not Meeting the Benchmark

These students do not correctly identify both Angles A and D as right angles and may identify Angle B or Angle D as right angles. Gil, for example, wrote:

A. Greater than 90 degrees

B. It is 90 degrees

C. Greater that 90 degrees

D. It is 90 degrees

Students like Gil need more experience comparing angles to known right angles (such as the corners of papers) and working with the "moveable angles" constructed with straws and connectors in Investigation 3.

The Space Is the Same

Students in this class have solved the Tetromino Puzzle (Session 2.3) and are sharing solutions. As the students discuss the way that Becky and Gil each formed the square tetromino, they consider how to measure the area of a shape.

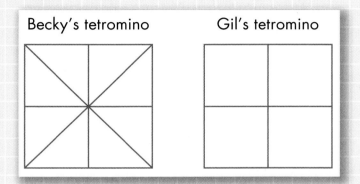

Becky: I made my square tetromino out of all the little triangles. It was twice as many—two and two and two and two—eight little triangles. So it has eight areas.

Teacher: But I thought that Gil said that the area of his square is four. Let's look at your square and Gil's. What do people think? Do these two have the same amount of space?

Nancy: They *are* the same amount, but hers has more pieces.

Kenji: The space is the same because two of the triangles make a square, so every time it's 2, 4, 6, 8, it's really like 1, 2, 3, 4 squares.

Becky: That's what I said. It's twice as many!

Zhang: But the square tetrominoes are the same size. If you moved Becky's square tetromino, it would fit right on top of Gil's. They're congruent!

Teacher: Becky, you said you made yours with twice as many pieces.

Becky: Uh-huh.

Teacher: Here's my question for everybody. What's the difference between counting the number of pieces, and saying what the area is in square units? Or is it the same thing?

Denzel: It's like the space is the same, but she made it differently.

Ines: You can make the same amount of space different ways. You could make tiny, tiny pieces and still cover up the square. It's still the same size.

Becky: But I used eight of the little triangles to make the square tetromino. So why isn't it eight?

Teacher: Can someone answer Becky's question?

Kenji: Well, it's like you could say that the square tetromino is made of eight triangles. But we want to know how many squares it is. Two of the little triangles makes one square, so it's like I said before, two triangles is one square, four triangles is two squares, like that. The eight triangles that Becky used are equal to four squares.

Teacher: So, we *could* have decided to measure the area in triangles, but we decided to use square units. That's partly because when people are measuring a flat space like this, they usually use square units to measure.

The teacher asks Becky to talk about why she thinks her square has an area of eight. He understands that in one sense, Becky is correct—one way to describe the area of the square tetromino is by saying "eight triangles". However, because students already know the tetromino has an area of four square units, the teacher wants to focus the discussion on two ideas—the area of both shapes is the same and a square unit is a standard unit of measure for area.

Finding Perimeter and Area

In Sessions 2.5 and 2.6, students have been finding the perimeter and area of their own footprints. The teacher has been watching and interacting with students, asking what strategies they are using to find perimeter and area, and if they are making certain to include all of the perimeter, or all of the area. In this discussion, the teacher focuses on how students found the perimeter and area.

Teacher: Let's start by talking about perimeter. Who will describe how they found the perimeter of their footprint?

Edwin: I measured the squares.

Teacher: Hmmm, Edwin how did you use the squares to find perimeter?

Edwin: I just counted all the squares and that was it.

Teacher: What do the rest of you think?

Pilar: I think that works, but I thought squares were area.

Edwin: Oh! That's right, that's how I found the area, not the perimeter!

Teacher: OK, but let's talk about perimeter. Who wants to explain what they did?

Cameron: I just put yarn around my footprint. Then I measured the yarn.

Dwayne: I did perimeter and I used the handle of the marker container thing and half of my foot was nine inches and the other half was $9\frac{1}{2}$ inches.

Teacher: Any questions for Cameron or Dwayne?

Keisha: Yes, I want to know how Dwayne figured out the whole perimeter.

Dwayne: Nine and nine is 18 inches and then 18 inches plus a $\frac{1}{2}$ inch is $18\frac{1}{2}$ inches.

Teacher: How about the part that goes around your heel or toes?

Dwayne: I got that. It was part of the half.

Teacher: So it sounds like one of the challenging things with perimeter was figuring out how to make a straight line so you could measure it. How about the area? Who wants to explain how they found the area of their foot?

Gina: I tried to find the column and rows but some aren't full. I wasn't sure what to do.

Nancy: First I copied my foot onto grid paper. Then I counted all the whole squares, then the halves. I got 22 square units.

Teacher: Nancy, why did you use grid paper?

Nancy: Well, at first I just did it because I saw Chiang doing it, but then I figured out I needed to have squares on the paper so I could count them!

Nicholas: I did that too, but then I saw like a rectangle in my footprint, so I drew the lines on it. There were four in each row, and six rows, so I got 24 squares, then added on the others.

Teacher: So it sounds like the challenging part of the area is how to count those partial squares. How did people count the partial squares?

Deondra: I judged them with my eyes and I'd think [points to different partial squares on her footprint] this one and this one make about a whole, and this one and this one. Like that. [A number of students nod in agreement.]

Adam: I didn't even count them. I just counted the whole squares.

Keisha: You can't do that! You have to count them!

Adam: Why?

Keisha: You just have to! [pauses] Hmm. It's just like when we did the tetrominoes. You have to cover everything; you can't have any gaps. So you have to count everything on the foot.

Teacher: Good. We have to count everything. I noticed just about everyone ended up tracing their footprints on grid paper. Here's my last question. Was doing that helpful for finding area or perimeter?

Oscar: Area, because it would work just as easily on a plain piece of paper for perimeter because you're just finding the outside of it. It doesn't matter if there are squares or not. But for area, you need some kind of square units to count.

During the course of this discussion, the teacher wants students to focus on some important ideas about perimeter and area and how they are measured—that perimeter is a one-dimensional or linear measure (even if the border is curved) and that area is two-dimensional and measured in square units. Since many students confuse perimeter and area, the teacher highlights the difference between the two measures. The teacher does not focus on the exactness of students' measurements (such as not worrying about how much the yarn stretches out, or if each partial square that students count as $\frac{1}{2}$ a square unit is actually $\frac{1}{2}$, etc.). His goal in this discussion is for students to understand that "everything" has to be measured. Therefore, he asks Dwayne about accounting for the heel and the toes in finding perimeter, and highlights for the whole class Keisha's explanation about having to count the partial squares.

Building a Definition of Triangles

Students are discussing the Tricky Triangles activity in Session 3.2, in which they decide if certain figures are or are not triangles. They first discuss figure N, which most students agree is not a triangle. Adam, however, has a different opinion.

Adam: I think this shape counts because it's actually *two* triangles.

Becky: But you can't say that because it's supposed to be just one shape, and this one crosses itself.

Dwayne: Plus it has more than three sides—I think it really has four sides.

Teacher: Adam, do you see what Dwayne means when he says four sides? Where are they?

Adam: Oh, I guess you could think of the X in the middle as two sides that cross. Or you could say that this shape has six sides—three for each triangle. So I guess it can't be just one triangle.

The class looks at figure O next.

Keisha: That's not a triangle! It's too skinny!

Benjamin: Yes, it's too far up. The lines are going too close in the same direction.

Jane: And if you stood the two tall sides up, then the bottom side wouldn't be straight (*horizontal*).

Teacher: Does anyone think this could be a triangle?

Bridget: It looks like the triangle our large flip-chart makes with the desk, so it must be a triangle.

Edwin: It is too a triangle. It's a closed shape, and it's got three straight sides and three corners.

Teacher: Edwin, it sounds like you're using the definition we came up with on our chart about what triangles have. Did anyone else use that chart?

Several students nod.

Teacher: We can keep that in mind as we continue. Let's look at another shape that people had questions about.

Gil: That's not a triangle because it's upside down.

Kathryn: But what's that word for same size and same shape?

Teacher: Congruent?

Kathryn: Right, and if you turn this triangle over, it would still be congruent.

Teacher: To what?

Kathryn: To this triangle [turning the triangle until it is oriented with a horizontal base]—to itself! So if it's a triangle one time, it must be all the time.

In this discussion, students are using what they know about triangles, as well as the mental images they have associated with triangles, to make their arguments. As students make statements that are not correct, the teacher asks for other opinions, without evaluating them. This gives students the opportunity to defend their opinions, and in some, but not all cases, to convince each other of the properties that define a triangle. The teacher also knows that as students continue to think about these questions, they are able to further develop their ideas before the next discussion.

Student Math Handbook

The *Student Math Handbook* pages related to this unit are pictured on the following pages. This book is designed to be used flexibly: as a resource for students doing classwork, as a book students can take home for reference while doing homework and playing math games with their families, and as a reference for families to better understand the work their children are doing in class.

When students take the *Student Math Handbook* home, they and their families can discuss these pages together to reinforce or enhance students' understanding of the mathematical concepts and games in this unit.

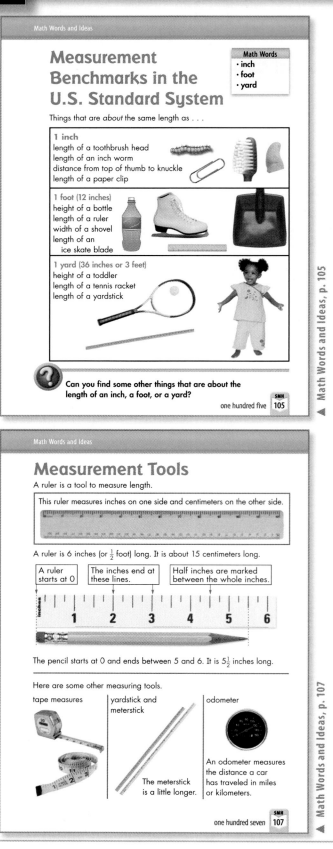

Math Words and Ideas

Measurement Benchmarks in the U.S. Standard System

Math Words
• inch
• foot
• yard

Things that are *about* the same length as . . .

1 inch
length of a toothbrush head
length of an inch worm
distance from top of thumb to knuckle
length of a paper clip

1 foot (12 inches)
height of a bottle
length of a ruler
width of a shovel
length of an ice skate blade

1 yard (36 inches or 3 feet)
height of a toddler
length of a tennis racket
length of a yardstick

? Can you find some other things that are about the length of an inch, a foot, or a yard?

one hundred five **105** SMH

▲ Math Words and Ideas, p. 105

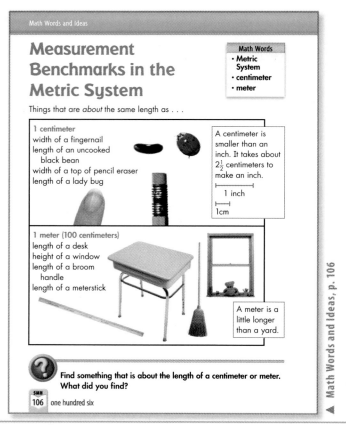

Math Words and Ideas

Measurement Benchmarks in the Metric System

Math Words
• Metric System
• centimeter
• meter

Things that are *about* the same length as . . .

1 centimeter
width of a fingernail
length of an uncooked black bean
width of a top of pencil eraser
length of a lady bug

A centimeter is smaller than an inch. It takes about $2\frac{1}{2}$ centimeters to make an inch.

1 inch
1cm

1 meter (100 centimeters)
length of a desk
height of a window
length of a broom handle
length of a meterstick

A meter is a little longer than a yard.

? Find something that is about the length of a centimeter or meter. What did you find?

SMH **106** one hundred six

▲ Math Words and Ideas, p. 106

Math Words and Ideas

Measurement Tools

A ruler is a tool to measure length.

This ruler measures inches on one side and centimeters on the other side.

A ruler is 6 inches (or $\frac{1}{2}$ foot) long. It is about 15 centimeters long.

A ruler starts at 0

The inches end at these lines.

Half inches are marked between the whole inches.

inches **1   2   3   4   5   6**

The pencil starts at 0 and ends between 5 and 6. It is $5\frac{1}{2}$ inches long.

Here are some other measuring tools.

tape measures

yardstick and meterstick

odometer

The meterstick is a little longer.

An odometer measures the distance a car has traveled in miles or kilometers.

one hundred seven **107** SMH

▲ Math Words and Ideas, p. 107

160 UNIT 4 | Perimeter, Angles, and Area

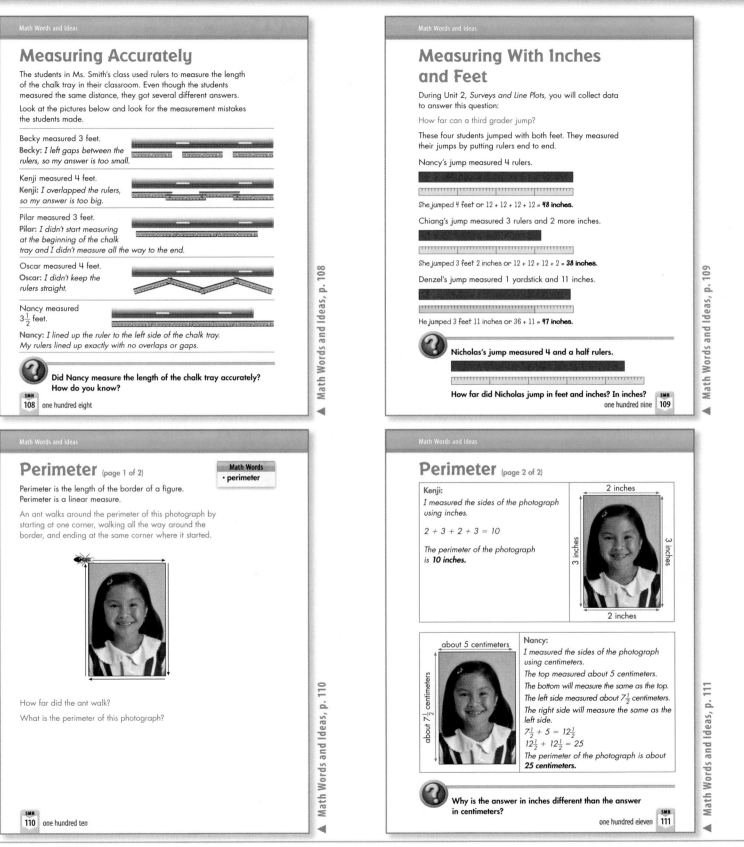

Math Words and Ideas

Measuring Accurately

The students in Ms. Smith's class used rulers to measure the length of the chalk tray in their classroom. Even though the students measured the same distance, they got several different answers.

Look at the pictures below and look for the measurement mistakes the students made.

Becky measured 3 feet.
Becky: *I left gaps between the rulers, so my answer is too small.*

Kenji measured 4 feet.
Kenji: *I overlapped the rulers, so my answer is too big.*

Pilar measured 3 feet.
Pilar: *I didn't start measuring at the beginning of the chalk tray and I didn't measure all the way to the end.*

Oscar measured 4 feet.
Oscar: *I didn't keep the rulers straight.*

Nancy measured $3\frac{1}{2}$ feet.
Nancy: *I lined up the ruler to the left side of the chalk tray. My rulers lined up exactly with no overlaps or gaps.*

Did Nancy measure the length of the chalk tray accurately? How do you know?

108 one hundred eight

◀ Math Words and Ideas, p. 108

Math Words and Ideas

Measuring With Inches and Feet

During Unit 2, *Surveys and Line Plots,* you will collect data to answer this question:

How far can a third grader jump?

These four students jumped with both feet. They measured their jumps by putting rulers end to end.

Nancy's jump measured 4 rulers.

She jumped 4 feet or 12 + 12 + 12 + 12 = **48 inches.**

Chiang's jump measured 3 rulers and 2 more inches.

She jumped 3 feet 2 inches or 12 + 12 + 12 + 2 = **38 inches.**

Denzel's jump measured 1 yardstick and 11 inches.

He jumped 3 feet 11 inches or 36 + 11 = **47 inches.**

Nicholas's jump measured 4 and a half rulers.

How far did Nicholas jump in feet and inches? In inches?

one hundred nine **109**

◀ Math Words and Ideas, p. 109

Math Words and Ideas

Perimeter (page 1 of 2)

Math Words
• **perimeter**

Perimeter is the length of the border of a figure. Perimeter is a linear measure.

An ant walks around the perimeter of this photograph by starting at one corner, walking all the way around the border, and ending at the same corner where it started.

How far did the ant walk?

What is the perimeter of this photograph?

110 one hundred ten

◀ Math Words and Ideas, p. 110

Math Words and Ideas

Perimeter (page 2 of 2)

Kenji:
I measured the sides of the photograph using inches.

$2 + 3 + 2 + 3 = 10$

The perimeter of the photograph is **10 inches.**

2 inches
3 inches
3 inches
2 inches

Nancy:
I measured the sides of the photograph using centimeters.
The top measured about 5 centimeters.
The bottom will measure the same as the top.
The left side measured about $7\frac{1}{2}$ centimeters.
The right side will measure the same as the left side.
$7\frac{1}{2} + 5 = 12\frac{1}{2}$
$12\frac{1}{2} + 12\frac{1}{2} = 25$
The perimeter of the photograph is about **25 centimeters.**

about 5 centimeters
about $7\frac{1}{2}$ centimeters

Why is the answer in inches different than the answer in centimeters?

one hundred eleven **111**

◀ Math Words and Ideas, p. 111

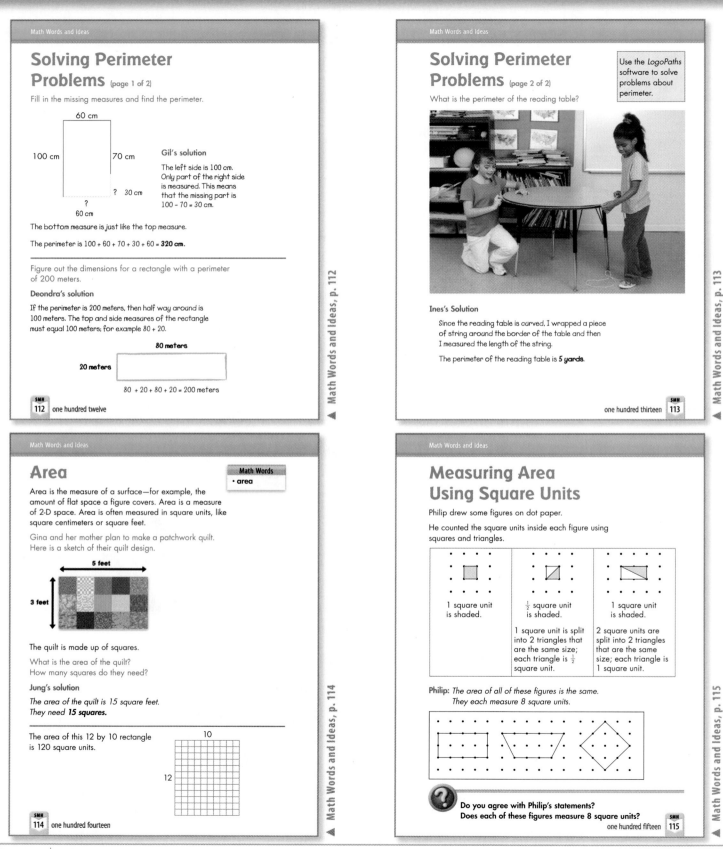

Solving Perimeter Problems (page 1 of 2)

Fill in the missing measures and find the perimeter.

60 cm

100 cm   70 cm

?   30 cm

?

60 cm

Gil's solution

The left side is 100 cm.
Only part of the right side
is measured. This means
that the missing part is
100 – 70 = 30 cm.

The bottom measure is just like the top measure.

The perimeter is 100 + 60 + 70 + 30 + 60 = **320 cm.**

Figure out the dimensions for a rectangle with a perimeter
of 200 meters.

Deondra's solution

If the perimeter is 200 meters, then half way around is
100 meters. The top and side measures of the rectangle
must equal 100 meters; for example 80 + 20.

80 meters

20 meters

80 + 20 + 80 + 20 = 200 meters

112 one hundred twelve

◀ Math Words and Ideas, p. 112

Solving Perimeter Problems (page 2 of 2)

Use the *LogoPaths*
software to solve
problems about
perimeter.

What is the perimeter of the reading table?

Ines's Solution

Since the reading table is curved, I wrapped a piece
of string around the border of the table and then
I measured the length of the string.

The perimeter of the reading table is **5 yards.**

one hundred thirteen **113**

◀ Math Words and Ideas, p. 113

Area

Math Words
• area

Area is the measure of a surface—for example, the
amount of flat space a figure covers. Area is a measure
of 2-D space. Area is often measured in square units, like
square centimeters or square feet.

Gina and her mother plan to make a patchwork quilt.
Here is a sketch of their quilt design.

5 feet

3 feet

The quilt is made up of squares.

What is the area of the quilt?
How many squares do they need?

Jung's solution

*The area of the quilt is 15 square feet.
They need* **15 squares.**

The area of this 12 by 10 rectangle
is 120 square units.

10

12

114 one hundred fourteen

◀ Math Words and Ideas, p. 114

Measuring Area Using Square Units

Philip drew some figures on dot paper.

He counted the square units inside each figure using
squares and triangles.

1 square unit is shaded.	$\frac{1}{2}$ square unit is shaded.	1 square unit is shaded.
	1 square unit is split into 2 triangles that are the same size; each triangle is $\frac{1}{2}$ square unit.	2 square units are split into 2 triangles that are the same size; each triangle is 1 square unit.

Philip: *The area of all of these figures is the same.
They each measure 8 square units.*

**Do you agree with Philip's statements?
Does each of these figures measure 8 square units?**

one hundred fifteen **115**

◀ Math Words and Ideas, p. 115

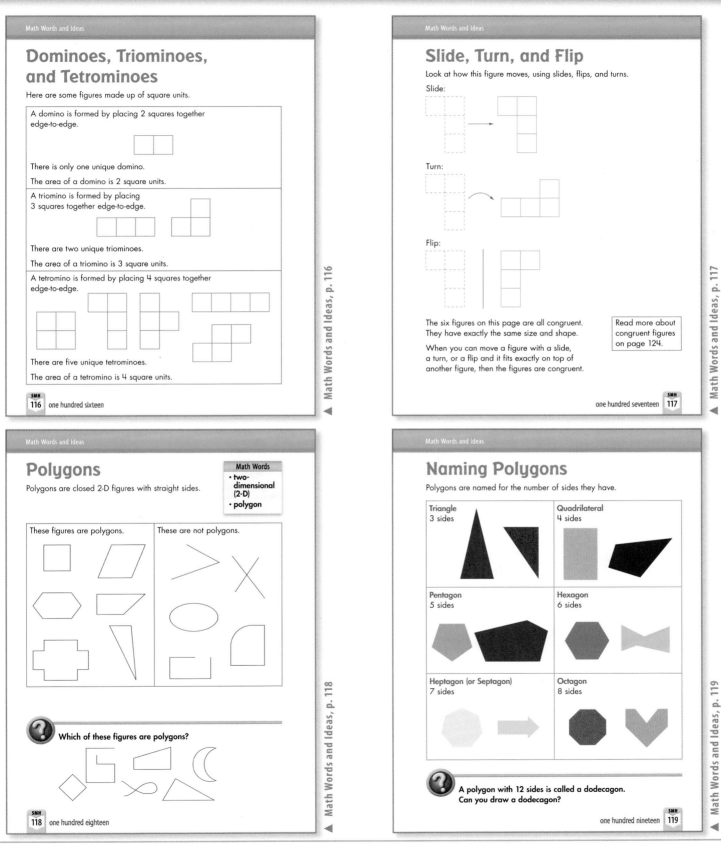

Dominoes, Triominoes, and Tetrominoes

Here are some figures made up of square units.

A domino is formed by placing 2 squares together edge-to-edge.

There is only one unique domino.

The area of a domino is 2 square units.

A triomino is formed by placing 3 squares together edge-to-edge.

There are two unique triominoes.

The area of a triomino is 3 square units.

A tetromino is formed by placing 4 squares together edge-to-edge.

There are five unique tetrominoes.

The area of a tetromino is 4 square units.

116 one hundred sixteen

◄ Math Words and Ideas, p. 116

Slide, Turn, and Flip

Look at how this figure moves, using slides, flips, and turns.

Slide:

Turn:

Flip:

The six figures on this page are all congruent. They have exactly the same size and shape.

When you can move a figure with a slide, a turn, or a flip and it fits exactly on top of another figure, then the figures are congruent.

Read more about congruent figures on page 124.

one hundred seventeen **117**

◄ Math Words and Ideas, p. 117

Polygons

Polygons are closed 2-D figures with straight sides.

Math Words
• two-dimensional (2-D)
• polygon

These figures are polygons. | These are not polygons.

? Which of these figures are polygons?

118 one hundred eighteen

◄ Math Words and Ideas, p. 118

Naming Polygons

Polygons are named for the number of sides they have.

Triangle
3 sides

Quadrilateral
4 sides

Pentagon
5 sides

Hexagon
6 sides

Heptagon (or Septagon)
7 sides

Octagon
8 sides

? A polygon with 12 sides is called a dodecagon. Can you draw a dodecagon?

one hundred nineteen **119**

◄ Math Words and Ideas, p. 119

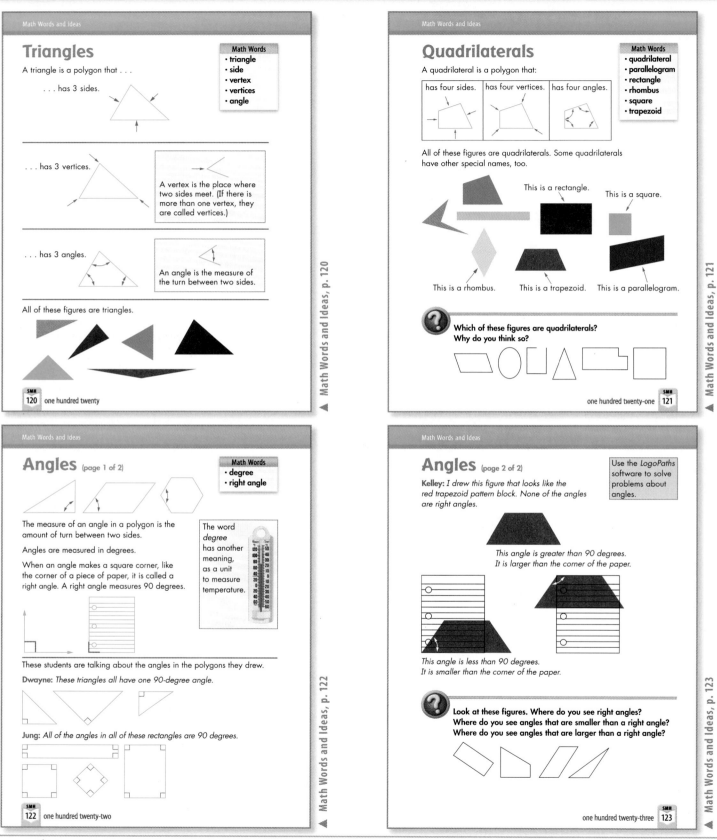

Index